# The Old Person in Your Home

# The Old Person in Your Home

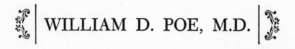 WILLIAM D. POE, M.D.

NEW YORK

CHARLES SCRIBNER'S SONS

# Foreword

This book is intended for all who face the responsibility of caring for the elderly, but particularly for those in situations where two or more generations live together. It is based on my own experience, accumulated during eighteen years as a family doctor with a practice that included thousands of elderly patients and provided me with knowledge of the home situations of the elderly and their relatives at all hours of the day and night, in all stages of illness, and in all seasons of the year. Some of the more intimate details come from personal as well as professional experience, since my aged mother has made her home with me.

In discussing the elderly I prefer to individualize them by such terms as Grandmother, Grandfather, Aunt Caroline, Uncle George, and the like—I refuse to refer to "senior citizens" or use such honeyed phrases as "golden years" or "sunset years."

Obviously no book can answer all questions regarding the aged and their problems. My aim is merely to frame the right questions so that answers may be sought calmly, deliberately, and in advance. For suggestions on problems that arise in day-to-day living, refer to the table of contents and the index. Outside sources of help are listed in the appendix.

A book is no substitute for a physician, but I hope this one may lessen the anxiety of older patients and those who care for them and make the doctor's work a little easier.

WILLIAM D. POE, M.D.

# Contents

# The Old Person in Your Home

# ❦ 1 ❦

# How Elderly People Contribute to Family Life

Many grandparents and great-grandparents ask, in moments of illness or hopelessness, "Why can't I just die peacefully?" Tired, discouraged, or selfish children have often asked, "Why doesn't she just go ahead and pass on?" Of course these questions have no easy answer. Illness, invalidism, defeat, and death—in the aged as in war—bring out the worst as well as the best traits in human character. But I have learned over the years that elderly people are important in modern American life. In a changing world the helpless aged as well as the helpless young give us a sense of responsibility and a feeling of continuity.

Consider some of the practical applications. I know a family whose way of life is hopelessly cramped by the financial burden of caring for an obdurate grandmother who is incapable of change. Although she lives in a distant city, her presence is felt constantly. Father, mother, in-laws, teenagers, even third-graders have come to resent the existence of the burden. What a nice vacation they could have, what a nice car, what a better house would be theirs—but for Grandmother.

On analysis, though, the members of this family, who do not get along too well with one another anyway, are more united because of their common concern than they would otherwise be. It may be unfair to the elderly relative, but in a way this is what holds the family together, and perhaps the children, if not the parents, will learn to meet responsibility with grace and to show compassion ungrudgingly.

In another family, not nearly so well off, the children are taught patience, sacrifice, and loving kindness out of consideration for a ninety-year-old grandparent. These qualities will enrich their whole lives.

In a fragmented society, prone to selfishness and rootlessness, if we will but heed, the old show us the need for gentleness, patience, kindness, and unselfishness. I submit that any social force which calls upon such traits makes a definite contribution to the national life.

A very old and wise physician once told me that the main thing the elderly can teach the young is serenity. Anyone who has observed adolescents knows that they frequently attach importance to what may seem trivial in the long run. The special problems of middle age may cause some people to make foolish decisions. The aged, having lived through these trying periods, can often give reassurance to the troubled. Too often people fail to grasp the support which the elderly are able to give.

Old age should be a time of learning what not to do. An old person who has learned this lesson has a great deal to teach us about becoming too much absorbed in busy work which costs more in physical and nervous energy than the results are worth. This art of not doing is learned with difficulty. It is the essence of growing old gracefully; it is the secret of contentment instead of frustration.

A prominent man, well along in years, when called upon to make a speech, politely declined, saying, "Thank you for asking, but you know, I have to husband my energy." Such an old person can perhaps teach a distraught housewife to husband hers, too, or a self-important businessman to conserve his strength.

In this process of learning to not do, serenity can be achieved. A very able elderly woman, reduced in physical energy, once said, "I know why I'm living so long. I've got to live long enough to learn to let God and St. Peter run things in heaven without my butting in."

Many elderly people do not retreat from life's battles; they merely withdraw from the front lines. Many of my patients have taken part-time jobs, developed hobbies, traveled, or become involved in religious or civic work. In maintaining mental flexibility, in meeting personal and community needs, they have much to teach.

Too often, a younger person does not take time to learn from the elderly because of disdain, or even scorn, for their old-fashioned ways. I have seen people show impatience when an elderly person preferred to pay cash for medical service, rather than impose on a secretary who would have the job of mailing out a statement. Younger people don't realize that the elderly are more aware of death and want their accounts paid up to date to save needless trouble. This sort of consideration is another thing the young can learn from the old.

While it is difficult to determine where orderliness leaves off and fussiness begins, in visiting thousands of homes I have noticed that an added degree of orderliness makes for added comfort. Let us, by all means, add orderliness to the virtues the old can teach us.

There are others, not the least of which is religious faith. Yet I have known people of grace and substance who don't take the religious observances of the elderly seriously, even if they may refrain from outward scorn.

The old can give us all a sense of continuity. It is touching to see how much they love their own kin, particularly grandchildren and other children in the family. I know a grandfather who regularly takes his daily constitutional by helping his grandson on the youngster's morning-paper route and a grandmother who helps her grandson to fold his papers preparatory to going on his route. Another elderly lady helps her niece with sewing. Still another grandmother is the most civilizing influence on a boisterous twelve-year-old boy, who treats her with a tenderness he shows to no one else.

The feeling of kinship is an important asset in any family. It is a natural characteristic, painfully observed in orphans, to want to know where we came from. A grandparent can provide this sense of continuity far better than a parent.

The elderly, generally, are more appreciative of small attentions than are people of any other age group. They are more generous with compliments than younger people are. Fairly often one sees an old man or woman whose entire life is dedicated to radiating sweetness.

I could give many more examples of contributions that the aged can make; the lessons they can teach are beyond enumeration. The usefulness of the aged must be appreciated; they must be respected and treated with dignity. We should all look upon old people as unique children of God and not put them into categories as being quaint, useless, outdated, and unworthy of patience and respect.

# ❦ 2 ❦

# Understanding the Elderly

The heading of this chapter might seem to suggest that old people are a different kind of beings—not really people at all. Someone defined old age as a dirty trick. And a wise person once said, "Mama is like she always was—only more so."

Understanding can be increased, however, by putting oneself in the place of an elderly person. Suppose you had lost your teeth, half your eyesight, a fourth of your hearing, and more than half of your ability to move around quickly. Suppose you were troubled about becoming a burden, about whether you had enough money, and about losing your ability to attend to business affairs. At any age, such handicaps would cause a great deal of anxiety; in this way old people are like the rest of us.

Suppose you were confronted with living in someone else's home, with little or no influence on ordinary day-to-day matters. Imagine finding yourself in a household where there was constant commotion and where the heating system was inadequate for your needs. Suppose also that you were in pain much of the time, your digestive functions were un-

7

comfortable, you didn't like the cooking, and you were constantly tired and slept poorly at night.

To think of yourself in such a position and with such impaired functions will help you to keep a realistic point of view toward the behavior of the aged.

It is unfortunate that, when confronted with deterioration of mind and body, many old people cannot help showing their anxieties in ill temper and spitefulness. They develop obsessions that they are going to catch pneumonia, or won't have a satisfactory bowel movement, or that a breath of fresh air may be a deadly draft. In extreme cases they may sink into a mute depression and have no regard for their person or surroundings. Making any decision is painful for them. Even such a simple question as "Do you want peas or beans for dinner?" can cause anxiety.

In this state of tension old people may get notions of being unloved or unwanted, and this is when they need the most patience and understanding.

Often the old feel lonely and depressed because they are treated as if they were pieces of furniture, or as if they were deaf and dumb. Many times I have had to silence an anxious daughter who was discussing her mother's condition as if the latter were not in the room. No one, at any age, likes to hear the details of his or her personal life talked about without being allowed to participate.

Most of us have a need to control our surroundings. If we cannot accomplish this in other ways, we may have temper tantrums, pout, show spitefulness or impatience, and display various physical symptoms. This sort of behavior occurs in the old as it does in the very young. With both, kind but firm discipline is required to see that it is not given too much rein.

All human beings, and especially the old, are apt to be

fickle, so don't expect always to get the same response to a particular suggestion.

Unless they are weak or really sick, most old people do not want people hovering about to give them their medicine or to fasten a button. Like other adults, they prefer to sit or eat or dress without having to endure the nervous, abrupt attempts by others to "help."

However, the reluctance to cast aside responsibilities, if carried too far, may be a source of physical danger. Aunt Adeline refused to quit carrying heavy laundry bags up the cellar steps until one day she had a heart attack and nearly died. Many aged persons have been injured as a result of climbing stepladders or standing on chairs.

I have mentioned the sense of orderliness in the old. Perhaps because disorder exacts a price in pain, most elderly persons like a regular routine and dislike change. They don't like to be moved or have their belongings scattered. An elderly woman who objected at first to going to a nursing home to recover from an illness was later reluctant to leave. "I like the orderliness here," she explained. "At your house I never know when it is mealtime."

A harmless family fuss can be disastrous to an old person. Violence, sadness, undue commotion, calamity in the house—or even on television—can often completely unnerve him.

It is painful to an elderly person to have his values ignored or scorned. If Grandfather hates liquor, drinking usually can be avoided in his presence. If Grandmother can't tolerate cigarette smoke, possibly some rules about smoking in her presence could be made. If tight slacks and scanty bathing suits shock her, she might be spared such exhibitions.

Not all the traits and kinds of behavior that I have

been describing will be found in every individual, of course, but they are characteristic of old people in general. If we realize and understand this and are prepared for it, it will be easier to be patient and to give the old person in our care the sympathy, the love, and the feeling of being needed that mean more than any amount of material luxury.

# { 3 }

# Our Obligations to Them

What do we owe, as a matter of right and decency in a rich country, to the elderly population who will number some twenty-five million by 1980?

Every advanced religion and ethical concept demands that we honor the aged. The Fifth Commandment says: "Honor thy father and thy mother." The New Testament commands: "Obey your parents." I believe that these biblical admonitions could now be translated to mean that we should have respect for the elderly as persons and be sensitive to their needs.

To hear a middle-aged and prosperous son or daughter speak disparagingly of aged parents is distressing. It is our obligation, I believe, to treat the elderly with kindness and respect and not reject them emotionally or physically. Acceptance and rejection are delicate matters in close human relationships. The elderly may feel rejection even when none is intended; therefore, extra efforts should be made.

In my medical practice I have been depressed by hearing people play the "if only" game. This is a game indulged in when people are tired and discouraged, and it is un-

pleasant indeed. "If Uncle John would only not be so
slow . . ."; "If only Grandfather would not smoke his
pipe . . ."; "If only I didn't have Mom to take care of,
John and I could go to Las Vegas. . . ." These are signs of
rejection and are unworthy of us.

We sometimes excuse unkind attitudes toward the
elderly by recalling their past faults or shortcomings. Is it
our place to punish a feeble grandfather for past errors by
abuse and neglect?

A good plan is to start each day, if not each hour, with
a clean slate, without a hint of disrespect, frustration, or
repudiation.

What of our material obligations to the elderly?

I once was called to a dirt-floored shanty to see a poor,
lonely, wooden-legged man. There was no electric light. A
small coal stove heated the tiny, ill-ventilated hovel to a
stifling degree. The smell of turnip greens pervaded the atmosphere. But the old man was cheerful, and as we talked I
learned that he had for a time been a patient at a nearby
Veterans Hospital. There had been Red Cross ladies and
aides to provide for his every need and whim. "Do you mean
to tell me," I asked him, "that you left Veterans Hospital to
come back to this shack? Why?"

He answered, "It's this way, Doc. It jes' war'n't home
there."

Our view of our obligations may miss the mark entirely. Let's try, insofar as possible, to list them in the same
order as the elderly person would list his needs. To this
humble old man his own shack and turnips were more
important than central heating and an antiseptic, unfamiliar
atmosphere. An unfeeling, bossy do-gooder could see him
and, hell-bent upon duty, declare that he should return to
the Veterans Hospital. Yet his material needs could be sup-

plied without removing him from the shack that to him was home.

As I see it, both we as individuals and society in general have an obligation to provide aging people with food, clothing, and shelter at a decent level of comfort, to assure needed medical care, and to give abundantly of understanding and compassion.

# { 4 }

# Their Social Needs

In any discussion of the social needs of the elderly it is well to remember that these needs vary almost as greatly as people in general. Some old people like company; some are more seclusive. Some enjoy commotion; most prefer tranquillity. Generally, talkative people become more talkative as they get older; quiet people become more quiet.

With rare exceptions, people of any age need the companionship of others with whom they can converse and exchange ideas. Old people do not enjoy people less because they are old. On the contrary, they are likely to enjoy them all the more. For happiness they must have people about them who understand their special problems and are sympathetic to them.

An old person especially needs to be recognized as part of the family and included in its concerns. The bleakest picture one can draw is that of a lonely old person relegated to a back room upstairs or a basement apartment where no one ever comes except to bring food and drink. Elderly people should not be put out of the way to avoid having them participate in activities or decisions which directly influence their life and comfort. Solitary confinement is not what they bargained for. Not even a criminal deserves such punishment.

Like anyone living within a family, Uncle George needs to feel that his wishes are heard, and that if they cannot be complied with he will be given some explanation. If he asks, "Could someone take me to the barber today?" he deserves more than "No time today!" He has a right to be told, "I'm sorry, Uncle George, but I've got to go to the P.T.A."

The proverbial bragging about grandchildren is evidence of the pride the old feel about their own descendants. Grandfather should be kept informed about the everyday comings and goings of the family, though without making him responsible for them. He should know that Jimmy is pitcher on his ball team, that Jane has a part in the school play, that Joe got the promotion in his job.

Grandparents have a right to meet a bride or groom coming into the family, even if they are incapable of going to the wedding.

While happy events should be shared with older people, they should if possible be spared family problems that may worry them. Misbehavior, poor school reports, and other such matters should be handled by parents, not grandparents, who nearly always have different ideas of discipline.

Old people need and enjoy the companionship of others of their own generation. Great capital is made of this in homes for the aged, retirement villages, retirement resorts, and the like.

If Grandfather or Grandmother has old friends living nearby, special efforts should be made to let them get together. A visit with a long-time associate provides great pleasure, and if Grandmother can discuss her real or fancied grievances with a comtemporary, family friction may be lessened.

Old people need to talk about their health, to discuss symptoms and operations. They gain renewal of hope from hearing of the recovery of one of their number from an operation or through a particular course of medical treatment.

Religious organizations can do a great deal to provide older people with diversion and companionship, although many do not do as much as they should in this way, and sometimes lack tact in what they do. One church which organized a club for the elderly called it the XYZ Club, suggesting that the members were reaching the end; actually the letters were intended to stand for "Extra Years of Zest." The club with this arresting name did real service. There were meetings twice a month for talk, book reviews, courses, knitting, ceramic making, and games, according to the interests and wishes of the members. Luncheon was served after the meeting. Such gatherings provide elderly people with social life and interests and lessen their dependence on children and grandchildren.

# ❧ 5 ❧

# Their Spiritual Needs

It may seem presumptuous in a physician to write about things of the spirit, a subject perhaps more appropriate to a minister. My observations have led me to a few simple conclusions which may help other people to understand the hope that offers meaning to the lives of the elderly.

Old people often raise questions concerning life and death: "Why do I live on, when some young person dies in the prime of life?" "Why do I live?" "Why can't I die?" "I wonder if I'll see my husband (or wife) in heaven?" "Is there a life beyond the grave?" "What is the meaning of existence?" They review mistakes of the past, admit to errors of long ago, and even try to make amends for misdeeds real or imagined. Such questioning indicates that people tend to become more philosophical as they grow older, even those who may have shown no such tendency in their younger days.

We all should be seeking answers to these questions; they only seem more urgent to the elderly. In the seeking, they may become more interested in scripture and devotional literature or poetry. This interest should be encouraged. Indeed, if it spills over to the rest of the family, all the better. I have known any number of families who have discovered the blessings of devotions. I have never known of any being hurt by them.

Sometimes the desire of old people to talk about death or past sins of omission or commission causes uneasiness in relatives. It shouldn't; let them talk. Talk like that is somehow a confessional which calms the spirit and renews the soul.

Often ministers are of great help in this soul-healing process, especially as sympathetic listeners.

According to her physical strength, upbringing, and inclination, your elderly mother should be encouraged to keep up her interest in church activities. It may seem a bother to accompany her to church, but the contact with the people there, the Mass or sermon, the quiet meditation, may be of vast importance to her well-being. Furthermore, a church service or group meeting is an occasion for her to dress up— to fix her hair and wear something stylish—all therapeutic measures for a person who wants to keep on enjoying life.

Visits by a pastor or a member of a church group can be very encouraging. If Grandfather has been sick, invite the minister to come by or to send someone from the church. Visits should be short, as too long visits can be tiring, but they can renew the aged spirit.

Occasionally, a self-righteous old person will use religion as an instrument for dominating the household rather than for sincere personal devotion. Such behavior has to be resisted. Household rules can be laid down about religious practice; Uncle James should not be allowed to make the family sit bolt upright while he discourses for thirty minutes on the minor prophets.

The old need to have their religious beliefs treated with respect. I have known grandparents who have been deeply hurt by the flouting of such values. Younger people are self-centered, and Grandfather may be ridiculed as a hopeless relic if he wants to go to Sunday school. While anger, disagreement, and resentment occasionally crop up in any home, these breaches can be healed, but ridicule of another person's sense of values causes wounds of the spirit which are almost beyond healing.

To members of certain faiths, last rites are important. Some people fear that administering the last rites to a person whose death is uncertain might hasten the end. I don't believe this is so; the devout and old do not really fear death and they are more likely to welcome the ceremony than to be alarmed by it.

I once had as a patient a very devout and seriously ill Catholic woman who was given extreme unction a half dozen times. Her poor ailing body continued to survive, somehow, and among priest, patient, and doctor a happy sort of joke developed about her trying to go to heaven, the priest trying to get her there, and my trying to delay the process. The large number of extreme unctions didn't hurt her at all.

The spiritual needs of the old are not really different from those that we all have, but the feeling that death is near makes these needs more important. By honoring them, we can contribute much to an aging person's peace of mind.

# ꜟ 6 ꜟ

# Their Financial Needs

In dealing with thousands of old people I have become aware that the difference between an amiable eccentric and an impossible old misanthrope is usually money. The problem is not confined to the old, but let us see how the impossible old misanthrope got that way.

Assume, if you will, that Mr. Sykes retired on a modest pension adequate for his needs at the time, but since then has had to pay the costs of his wife's long and extremely expensive illness, and he is now not only old and feeble but with just enough money to hold body and soul together. Perhaps he has been improvident or even wasteful, but this does not cure the gnawing bitterness in his heart that tells him that if he were financially comfortable he would not be suffering from indigestion or arthritis and could sleep better at night. He would not resent the son who had not appreciated his sacrifices in years past or hate that well-married daughter who had seemingly forgotten him completely.

The elderly poor usually feel that they are neglected because of their poverty—and too often they are right. Of course, they are wrong when they believe that money can buy health. The financially well-off old person has no such psychological pitfalls. When he suffers, he knows the pain has nothing to do with money.

Society in general measures a person by the property he has accumulated. The needs of rich old Mr. Brown and poor old Mr. Smith may be identical, but the chances are Mr. Brown's needs will be met long before Mr. Smith's. Fortunately, recent state and federal government programs have undertaken to narrow this difference, through Medicare, Medicaid, and Social Security benefits.

A steady and adequate income is a source of comfort to all human beings, old or young, sick and well, big-business barons or diggers of ditches. People sometimes think that by providing Grandmother with food and lodging they are doing all that is necessary. But whether she is living with relatives or not, an elderly lady should not have to ask for money to buy a spool of thread, or a book, or a new dress. If she does not have an adequate income, a fixed amount should be given to her by each of her children and working grandchildren. This offers a degree of self-respect and freedom which grudging handouts can't supply. It will allow her to get clothes, gifts, and other small items she may want. If she is in the mood to spend a little frivolously on perfume, lingerie, or a beauty-parlor treatment, so much the better; it is a sign that she considers herself a participant in the world of today.

I have discussed other needs elsewhere but the material and psychological importance of a steady income, however modest, is sometimes overlooked. The money should be given gladly and regularly. More often than not, it will save doctor's visits—and the bills besides.

To be free of money cares is perhaps the best medicine an old person can have.

# ⟨ 7 ⟩

# When to Start Living Together

In the preceding chapters I have tried to suggest some of the contributions, characteristics, problems, and needs of elderly people. Most of these exist whether an old person is living alone, with relatives, or in a home for the aged or a nursing home, and we all should take them into account in our relations with the old. Now I want to turn to the situation in which I hope this book will be especially helpful—that of sharing your home with an aging relative.

As a general rule, both the older generation and the younger are happier when they can live separately. However, many circumstances can occur to make it necessary or desirable for two or more generations to live together. Let me list some of these situations:

Elders are advanced in age and have suffered a setback in mental alertness or physical capabilities.

An aged husband or wife has died and the survivor is unable to deal with daily problems or unwilling to be alone.

It becomes financially impracticable or impossible to maintain a home just for one person.

The aged person or his family has reason to fear that injury or illness may come suddenly with no one at hand in an emergency.

Medical or nursing care cannot be carried out in the home of the elderly parent living alone.

An able-bodied grandfather or grandmother (or both) is needed to take care of home and grandchildren. This may happen when there is only one parent to support the family, when both parents must work outside the home, when there is illness in the family, or for other reasons.

Other considerations may also bring about such a move. An overly solicitous relative may be unwilling to let Mother live alone in peace because of a determination to "do something" for her. Social pressures may have influence, as when a prosperous son or financially well-married daughter does not want Mother or Father to go on living in a less desirable neighborhood. Or the move may be expected to solve any and all existing problems. (It won't.)

Whatever the reason for the decision to bring the elderly relative into your home, the wishes of the old person should be taken into account as far as possible. Old people should not be shoved about like pieces of furniture. But in many instances they cannot be allowed to make the final decision. The judgment of elderly, ailing, self-centered people is seldom the soundest. In addition, making a decision, particularly one that will have long-lasting effects, is very hard for the old. The thought of the move will raise such misgivings as:

Will I become a burden?
Will I become bedfast?
Do I have enough money to last my lifetime?

Will my children be good to me?
Will we get along well together?
What did so-and-so mean when he said so-and-so?
What causes this or that or so-and-so?
Suppose I'm wrong in making a move, what then?

Usually, the final decision must be made, after full consideration and preferably in consultation with other members of the family, by a level-headed son or daughter, whose affection for the old person is genuine.

When a decision has been reached, it should be presented as settled, not as a matter of choice. One should not say to a feeble old father, "Dad, how would you like to come and live with me, Josephine, and the children?" Rather, one should say, "Dad, we have been worried about you, and since you had that fall we have been getting a place ready for you at our house until you are well and strong again. Please let us decide this." This way of putting it relieves Grandfather of the burden of decision; it does not exclude the possibility of his getting better, and it shows consideration for his feelings.

In spite of a proper presentation and a genuine display of regard for how they may feel, elderly people can be cantankerous, of course, and flatly refuse to budge. In this case, the wise person will resort to other methods:

"Dad, we need you with us and you're going to come. Please don't get excited. Let's call in Dr. Jones and follow his advice."

"Dad, we want you to stay with us and have prepared a comfortable place, but if you won't come we'll have to call the health authorities. We cannot leave you here alone."

With the complicity of the physician, Dad can be put in a hospital and be found too sick to be sent home. He can then be brought to his new quarters by ambulance.

Legal proceedings may be started to commit the old person to the care of a relative. Thus an aged invalid will understand that matters are out of his hands.

Some of these measures may seem extreme, but they enforce a bit of discipline on a person who is apt to be governed solely by his whims and frustrations. Discipline, kind and loving, is as necessary for Aunt Sally's or Uncle Gilbert's or Mother's happiness as it is for anyone else's.

When possible, reject temporary arrangements. What seems easy and unimportant to a vigorous person is a great trial for a feeble one. Learning to use different light switches, door locks, and bathroom appliances is a great burden for old people. To keep adjusting to different people is even more difficult. Do not shunt an old person around from one relative to another, making him a stranger everywhere he goes, with no anchor anywhere, and a host of painful physical adjustments to make.

# { 8 }

# The Family Balance of Power

The addition of another adult to an existing family will always require adjustments by all concerned. When an older relative is brought into a home where tensions already exist, the effects may be disastrous, sometimes without anyone's realizing just what is happening. This unhappy development can come about because the balance of power is upset—a concept as valid in the domestic area as in the family of nations. A couple may have adjusted to their small conflicts so well that they are scarcely conscious of them, but the strains are present and the arrival of a third party may disturb the balance.

For example, John and Susan married against her mother's wishes. After a few violent arguments and a period of mutual adjustment, the two have been getting along well together, but John still resents Susan's mother and is not sure enough of his own position to accept her without suspicion. When she comes to live with them, the stage is set for John to criticize her unfairly and for Susan to rush to her defense. As a result, John may start drinking with his friends, while his mother-in-law sits at home with Susan, saying, "I always told you he was no good!"

Sometimes it is the husband's mother and the wife who have never liked each other. When the mother moves in and insists that the housekeeping be done *her* way, their ill feeling is aggravated and the home becomes a battleground.

Another threat to the balance occurs when Dad and his father are such close pals that the rest of the family is frozen out, or when Mother and her mother gang up to push Dad out of his position as head of the family. The strains may not be severe or dangerous but the signs are present, and a third party arriving on the scene can tip the balance.

The balance of power can be upset by money considerations. Jim and Jane have adjusted reasonably to marriage, although Jim has never made as much money as Jane's father. Then the old man moves in and wants to renovate the house according to his own plans. He has the money—therefore the right, he figures. Jane thinks this generous of her father, but Jim feels, rightly, that it threatens his command within his own home.

If Joe has difficulty setting rules and exerting healthy control over his adolescent children, his situation will not be helped by a doting grandmother who slips Junior extra money after his father has limited his allowance—with good reason.

Conflicts should be recognized and if possible resolved before inviting an older person to move in. If it is Joe's mother who tries to buy favor with the children, contrary to order and discipline, it is he who should say, "Mother, we have a responsibility for the children which we cannot turn over to you or anyone else. What I say may be wrong in your eyes, but since I'm the head of the family, you must let me be the one to give orders. We all love you, but you can surely understand that there can't be two captains on a ship."

If Jane's father tries to take over the household financially, she is the one who should say, "Daddy, we've been so happy here. We want to have you with us, but don't try to make us over."

As with any group endeavor, a household should have an acknowledged head. A power struggle can come about if the older person coming into the family is allowed to take charge. Ill-judged deference should not be an excuse for abdicating responsibility. The man of the family is the proper person to hold the reins. He will need to be strong, cool-headed, and fair-minded, as well as kind, loving, and considerate. With his wife's help, he can act as a benevolent despot. He must not allow his or his wife's aged parent to disrupt the home or interfere with discipline.

Grandparents seldom approve of the way discipline is maintained—in their judgment it is either too harsh or too mild. When unwanted advice is offered, father must say, firmly but with kindness, "Dad, I'm sorry, but this is my responsibility. I'm aking you to respect my rights just as I hope to respect yours."

Great harm can be done by a dominating elder whose powers have failed but whose strong will survives. If middle-aged people cower before aged tyrants, home can become a bedlam, with the incapable in command, the competent virtually straitjacketed, and the children trapped in a cross-fire of conflict. Father and mother must never abdicate their position of authority.

If mother, father, and children can talk freely, if disagreement can occur without bitterness and obedience without resentment—then and only then should the older folks be invited into the household.

Sometimes old people, merely by their presence, can

draw families closer together in sympathy, understanding, and love. The need to take care of a loved older person has caused people at the verge of estrangement to develop compassion for and communication with each other. In such cases the elders add light and beauty by their presence.

While the balance may be difficult to maintain at times, every member of the family should be alert to the danger of upsetting it. When this happens, all should strive to restore equilibrium.

# { 9 }

# Preparing for the Move

In planning to live together all members of the family should do a bit of soul-searching. In no other circumstances are people as apt to be contrary as when several generations take up living together in one household. At such a time the practice of kindness, gratitude, patience, love, understanding, generosity, and self-denial is of the greatest importance. Spite, ill-temper, selfishness, or willful behavior is most destructive when people share a home.

When a family is considering whether to have grandparents move in, the following questions should be raised:

Is this the best solution to the problem?

Are we doing it this way only because of what others might think?

Are we being selfish?

Are we more interested in *who* is right than *what* is right?

Are we ready to be kind and loving even when tired and upset?

Are we prepared to see it through, although we realize that we cannot succeed in making Dad (or Mother) happy, or even completely comfortable?

Are we willing to sacrifice to help our old folks feel secure and useful?

Are we physically able to care for an old person in our home?

Have we the skill to prepare special foods?

Will we be able to dress an old person who may be altogether helpless?

Is there adequate help to handle the house and nursing chores?

Do we have convenient bedroom and bathroom facilities?

Can we provide necessary privacy with another person in the house?

Will making an invalid grandparent the center of attention cheat youngsters out of the care or accommodations they need?

Will medical care and hospital service be available?

Will a move cause undue hardship by isolating the old person from familiar scenes and faces?

Will moving the old person too far from his place of worship cause him undue distress?

Will his new home provide adequately for exercise and recreational needs?

Can the old person adjust to living in a household of which he is not the head?

Is he a tyrant—or she a termagant—who cannot get along with other people?

Can all responsible members of the family agree that a move is best and contribute to its support personally and financially?

Can younger children be taught respect and kindness for Grandfather without feeling that they are being dominated?

If most of these questions can be answered satisfactorily a move has a fair chance of working. In answering them, however, make as sure as possible that the correct solutions are found. Family physicians have often witnessed disaster when decisions have been reached solely through the emotions, without careful thought given to what is involved. Most of such moves are fraught with at least as much chance of disturbance as is the arrival of a new baby. One must realize, however, that even after the most careful appraisal mistakes will be made.

Expect mistakes. Then you won't panic later when these become apparent. Maintain faith, and don't court calamity by piling more mistakes on top of those already made. Individuals will lose patience. There will be bad days. The patient will inevitably get worse instead of better. Do not assume the worst because of one bad day.

An important part of the psychological preparation for living with aged parents or relatives is to think in terms of developing a more or less "normal" routine. Few civilized people take delight in a topsy-turvy existence. Most people prefer some routine, and this is particularly necessary for old people. A plan should be worked out before, not after, the elderly parent arrives.

If the family cannot adjust to a measure of order regarding time of arising, mealtimes, bedtime, and responsibility for household chores, do not invite an old person to share chaos with you. Old people have a difficult time adjusting simply to a different order; they certainly cannot adjust to prevailing disorder. But neither should they be forced to adhere to a rigid schedule which is not of their making. Some flexibility on all sides is necessary for peace and comfort.

The younger folk must learn to be cheerful and optimistic in dealing with the old. Do not take a negative attitude. Avoid such remarks as: "The children are noisy and you'll have to learn to put up with it!" "We're going to be terribly crowded. It's too bad you can't stay at Jane's house. She has more room than we do." The chances are that your elderly parent or relative has already thought of too many reasons why things won't work. Instead, make hopeful, constructive suggestions: "Mama, you always liked roses. Tom wants you to help him in the garden." "Mama, we usually have to rush in the morning; it would be a big help if you could fix the lunches for the children." "Things are going to be so much better when you move in with us." "Dad, you won't have to worry about being snowed in during the winter." "Uncle Joe, your room is on the first floor. You won't have to go up and down stairs any more." "Aunt Edna, we need you—and you need us."

This last statement is perhaps the most important of all. Human beings need to feel wanted, and the loving expression of this need prepares an old person for what might be a traumatic move better than anything else you might think of.

Another means of psychological preparation is to allow Grandmother a hand in planning "her" room. Let her select drapery material, bedspread, and so on. If she is giving up an apartment or house, do not allow her to preside over the move. Decisions about what to take and what to leave are fraught with sadness, and at such times old people are likely to feel that they are being driven into exile against their will. Since not all objects can be kept, empha-

size the importance of the belongings which will be brought
to the new quarters.

Avoid disputes about unimportant details. A test of
wills usually leaves scars, and a temporary retreat on your
part will often bring about an easier agreement in the near
future.

# ❧ 10 ❧

# Arranging Living Quarters

Living arrangements should be thoroughly appraised for maximum comfort and convenience for everyone. It is not necessary that Grandfather have the best room in the house; he should have one that is convenient for nursing, and accessible—on the first floor if possible. Climbing stairs is a chore and can be a hazard; a fall can result in injuries that may be terminal.

Many people have turned a first-floor study or dining room into a bedroom; although such an arrangement may not afford ideal privacy, its convenience can more than make up for the lack. Privacy can be gained by the use of a folding screen or a draw curtain attached to the ceiling.

The room should be sunny and cheerful, with bright but not garish colors in walls, bedspreads, and draperies, and with ample and convenient lighting fixtures. Use familiar furnishings if possible. Old people feel more at home when they have things they are used to around them.

Chairs and bed should be firm, comfortable, and fairly high. Low overstuffed chairs are hard for the old to get out of. A bed that is too low is not as easy to get into and is not practical when nursing is required. However, a high hospital bed presents hazards in getting both in and out; these should be used only for bedfast patients.

Do not use small throw rugs. They can cause tripping, and even with rug cushions may slip and cause a nasty fall. Correct any unevenness in floors or rugs if possible.

A closet in the room is highly desirable. It should have a light and shelves that are easy to reach.

The room should have an adjacent toilet, or if possible a complete bathroom where medicines and sickroom supplies can be kept. In a bathroom used by an old person, a bar that offers a firm handhold should be attached to the wall over the tub. A bathtub seat makes a tub bath easier since it is then unnecessary for the patient to sit down in the tub. A small stool placed in a shower stall probably facilitates cleanliness better than anything. Make certain that bathroom floors and bathtubs are not slippery. Use strips of tape or grooved rubber pads for secure foothold.

Make sure that the room can be kept comfortably warm. Sometimes a small electric heater is needed but this should be placed where there is no danger of falling over it. In many areas an air conditioner would be a boon, particularly in keeping a bed patient comfortable in hot, humid weather. If the patient is lame, a stroller, which can be purchased at a department store or mail-order house, is a help in getting around. A wheel chair can also be of enormous use in getting a feeble person around the house. If the patient is very feeble he may need a safety belt to hold him securely in the chair—I know of a fatality that resulted from falling from a wheel chair.

A heating pad, enema bag, bedpan, and for men a urinal, will be necessary sooner or later. A tray with legs will make serving meals in bed less of a problem.

Other materials may be needed for special situations; these will be suggested under discussion of specific ailments.

One should recognize that considerable expense can be involved in getting a house ready for an elderly member of the family. The preceding suggestions are aimed at ideal arrangements, and in many cases compromises will be necessary. Not every adjustment has to be made before the move. Progress can be achieved as one goes along, but precautions against accidents are easier than bemoaning the results.

# ❧ 11 ❧

# Organizing the Household

A household usually makes some preparation for even the most casual visitor. It should prepare with special consideration for a permanent visitor, who may be a helper or an added responsibility, a ministering angel or an invalid who requires constant care.

In addition to the planning described thus far, it would be well to have every member of the family drilled a bit in his responsibilities to the guest and to the rest of the household.

Father should take the lead in this discussion. Since Mother will probably be the chief housekeeper, companion, and nurse, effort should be made to spare her as much as possible.

Has Mother been making up beds for teen-agers? Has she been picking up after grown sons and daughters? Has she been setting the table, when the children are old enough to take on such duties? If the answer to these questions is yes, then reassignment of these tasks should be made before Grandmother sets foot in the door.

Have people been skipping meals, sleeping late, not

getting to school on time? This kind of disorder unnerves old people and should be set to rights.

In consultation with Grandmother, decide in advance how she can be useful in her new home. Can she sort the laundry? Prepare breakfast? Set the table? Peel potatoes? Dust the living room? If she is able, she will probably want to take responsibility for her own room, apart from heavy cleaning. Grandfather may also be able to keep his room tidy.

Be sure that the division of labor is clear and does not make for warfare. Two women in the kitchen at the same time frequently end by colliding physically and emotionally—and the resulting bitterness spreads to the entire household and may even infect the food.

Grandparents can frequently give needed loving attention to youngsters when parents are too busy. As suggested earlier, they can be a civilizing influence as well. Adolescents can learn gentleness and consideration which influence their future behavior as mature prople.

If children are taught love and respect, they can be of enormous help to Grandfather and he can help them greatly as well. Can he carve or tinker? Does he like fishing or sports? Is he able to help out in the yard? Grandmother can often teach such skills as knitting, sewing, perhaps cookie making when Mother is not busy in the kitchen. Knitting mittens and making doll clothes are traditional activities of grandmothers.

Remember, failures are to be expected even with the most careful planning. Every day will not go smoothly. Individuals will lose patience or get sick. Grandmother may be upset at times. There will be occasional regret at the move. Make allowances for trying days. Try to avoid head-on contests of will. Start each new day with optimism.

Some families find an advantage in starting each day

with a devotional period when scripture, poetry, or inspirational literature is read aloud. Sometimes the elderly person can take charge of this interval, helping the family off to a good day's beginning. For those religiously inclined, prayers at some time during the day tend to reduce tensions.

All the adapting should not have to be done by grandparents. Everyone should be willing to adjust so that all can live contentedly together, and planning in advance will make the adjustment easier.

# ❦ 12 ❧

# Medical Preparation

Before the generations get together in one household, the health of all should be thoroughly checked. I have seen an aged tuberculous woman brought into a household of young children without the family's being aware that she was a serious menace—not because of the T.B., but because she didn't know she had it. She should have been checked particularly for contagion, diabetes, circulatory difficulties, urinary function, and anemia, since these have serious implications if not recognized. More important, every old person should have a personal physician to whom he or she can be taken regularly or who can make home visits.

A frank discussion with the doctor about emergency care could save a great deal of bitterness or possibly a life. Discuss the doctor's fees in a general way; expect to pay what is necessary. A discussion of your doctor's participation in various government and private health insurance plans would be in order too.

Arrangements should also be made for old people to have thorough dental care, and to have necessary checkups on vision and hearing.

The health of the younger generation is sometimes less robust than that of their elders. A frail, nervous, middle-aged woman who is barely able to keep going should not try to assume the care of an invalid. Occasionally an aging but still vigorous grandmother can be of great help in nursing a daughter or daughter-in-law. In this situation the same general rules apply; only the roles are reversed.

Be sure that strict regard is given to the health of children in the family. Some children are particularly subject to infections which may be brought in by an elder. Children may be carriers of the influenza virus which can be deadly to a feeble old person. Avoid such dangers with a program of annual *flu shots* for old and young; these will give partial protection.

To maintain the health of the entire household, provision should be made at the start for systematic recreation for all, especially for the chief breadwinner (usually father) and the head housekeeper (usually mother).

# ❧ 13 ❧

# Legal Preparation

When one assumes the care of an aged relative one takes on certain legal obligations as well. If the person's affairs are not in good order, these can be frustrating, annoying, time-consuming, and expensive.

Taxes must be paid if he owns property or has income. Bank deposits may have to be made and bills paid by check. There will be medical and hospital expenses to be met. Insurance premiums and forms must be attended to.

Real property may need to be disposed of. Strict accounts must be kept of all income, for tax purposes and so on. Even property given away should be accurately recorded.

Quite often, if a person is failing in mind or body, these routine matters become an extremely complicated task. In a complex society, it is difficult even for a vigorous person to understand business procedures; for most elderly people the problem becomes insuperable.

One way business affairs can be managed is for someone to take the responsibility of sitting down and going over details repeatedly to help an aging parent or in-law to get his books in order. As Grandmother becomes less confident, she will find this an unpleasant ordeal, enough to make her head swim and unsettle her completely.

At this stage it may be wise to suggest that she give someone a power of attorney. This is a document drawn up by a lawyer which legally allows her to designate someone else to manage her affairs. With such authority, a son, daughter, nephew, or other person can pay bills, write checks, sell property, and pay taxes without Grandmother's having to worry.

Unfortunately, many households do not work out such an arrangement and when an elderly parent has a serious illness and hospital bills are due, no one is empowered to pay except out of his own funds.

Sometimes the idea of giving power of attorney is resisted by a feeble oldster who may cling to the idea that he is more capable than he actually is. Admitting inability to cope with business procedure is sure to be painful. Here, an understanding lawyer or a trusted minister may be of help in arriving at a decision.

Everyone with possessions should have a will. This can be properly prepared only by a lawyer and if it has not already been done, should be attended to before a move. Often an aging person has definite ideas about funeral arrangements; if these are written into the will, later confusion and difficulty will be prevented.

When home furnishings must be disposed of before the move, the elderly person may wish to designate individuals who are to receive certain items. If so, well and good; but any dispute over them in the owner's presence should be suppressed; it can be very upsetting. Physicians have often encountered frankly expressed suspicion among relatives, to the extent that they seem like vultures waiting to pick a carcass—perhaps an ugly comparison, but no less distasteful than the actual wrangle of embittered relations over scraps of property.

Sometimes an old person who is unable to conduct business will flatly refuse to sign a power of attorney. There is a legal procedure, varying in different states, which allows constituted authority to appoint a committee to handle his affairs. This procedure is more complex than the appointment of a power of attorney but is likewise begun by an able lawyer.

In reviewing the old person's business, examine insurance policies. Are they to be kept or allowed to lapse? Do insurance policies have cash value which may be needed to pay expenses, or could be used to make home arrangements more comfortable? Is Grandfather receiving all the income to which he may be entitled by social security benefits, disability payments, or old-age insurance

This is the time to explore other sources of financial and physical assistance for which the old person under your care may be eligible. These are discussed in the following chapter.

# ✦ 14 ✦

# Resources Outside the Family

When you undertake the care of an aging person, you should face the fact that problems may arise which the family cannot deal with unaided.

Many people still feel that to accept help—except from a doctor, lawyer, or minister—is demeaning, but today, when society is beginning to acknowledge its debt to the elderly, such antiquated notions of "charity" are fortunately disappearing. The problem of the aged is universal and most people will need and should take advantage of all the help. they can get.

Part of the preparation for bringing an old person into your home is learning all you can about outside sources of help. A list of such sources is given in the Appendix of this book. Investigate them in advance. Eligibility for various kinds of services can be established before the need arises, and distress and delay at a time of emergency can be avoided.

Is your aged parent eligible for hospital or nursing home care from religious, fraternal, union, or government sources? Do you know how to get information about Medicare and other government programs? Are there local chapters of the American Heart Association, the American Cancer Society, the Arthritis Foundation, and others which can help with wheel chairs and other equipment, information, transportation to clinics, and other services? Where can you learn more about home nursing care?

One might think that Medicare, Medicaid, and the Administration on Aging would eliminate the need for volunteer health organizations. This is not true. The population is increasing, people are living longer, and medical knowledge and treatment are developing rapidly. Private organizations are being called on more than ever to continue their work in research, education, and services to individuals.

Even with the best efforts of private and public organizations, needs may go unmet. It is a blessing that both are working together.

One example, out of hundreds I could cite, is the case of an elderly patient of mine who developed cancer. I tried to reassure her but she became more fearful as the weeks passed. Her son, with whom she lived, wisely called the local chapter of the American Cancer Society requesting help. One of their volunteer workers, a gifted nurse, gladly went to see the patient—giving the needed encouragement, information, and affection. Later, when hospitalization was necessary, Medicare paid the bill which would have bankrupted the family. They were grateful for the help they received from both private and public services.

There are many organizations throughout the world that serve the elderly. The services offered by any single group are specialized, and the sheer number of agencies may be confusing. Therefore, it is necessary to know where to seek help to meet a particular need.

Thousands of people are employed by these organizations either as paid workers or as volunteers. In seeking help try to be concise in stating your problem, so that impatience and delays are minimized.

Remember, while most nongovernment organizations try to meet a request for help, they are not legally bound to do so. They are being asked a favor which they have a right to refuse.

In seeking help from those organizations listed in the Appendix, a few do's and don'ts are in order.

DO:

Seek help before an emergency develops.

Learn the rules of eligibility.

Be alert to the development of new resources and agencies which offer a needed service or which may be more convenient.

Avail yourself of all the services you need. If a promised service is not delivered, make continued courteous requests.

Contribute to private agencies when possible and encourage your friends to do so.

Show appreciation to those who help you. Generally they are underpaid or do it voluntarily.

Join with others who may have a similar problem to start a service if one is not already in your neighborhood.

DON'T:

Become overly dependent on others to meet your responsibility.

Waste the time of workers with needless calls and requests.

Expect of one agency what is the province of another.

Allow frustration or discourtesy to cause you to become upset.

Speak harshly of an approved agency because of a fault of one of its workers.

Be frustrated by what seem to be needless delays of service.

Allow prejudices against public health and welfare agencies to prevent your receiving services that you need and are entitled to.

## { 15 }

# First Days Together

Assume that everyone has prepared for the move, that order has been established, that medical and legal loose ends have been tied up, and that the living quarters have been made ready. Everything is as close to the ideal as possible. Does this mean that from now on things are bound to work happily and smoothly? It does not! Further human adjustments will still have to be made in the light of experience gained while living together.

The adjustments to be made by three generations in one house are nothing like those of a honeymoon, when differences dissolve merely because the individuals are in love. Instead of depending on mutual attraction, we must use judgment and patience to reduce irritations and hurt feelings.

Do not expect immediate harmony. A grandmother who has raised ten children will inevitably have something to say about disciplinary methods. She will have to learn not to undermine authority but tact can still be exercised. "Mom, we'll be responsible for disciplining the children. How would you like to bake Johnny a birthday cake? He'll be seven tomorrow." This is a definite suggestion and changes the subject so quickly that no one has time to sulk.

The would-be disciplinarian needs to be kept busy with a routine of her own, which will give her occupation and keep her from interfering too much with the regular running of the household.

It is only in day-to-day living that certain problems will show up and solutions be developed. How much help can Grandmother really give? Can Grandfather go for walks on his own or with the children? Can Uncle Joe drive a car? Can Aunt Jennifer be left in charge while Mother and Father go out for the evening, or go away on short trips?

The matter of driving a car may be a special problem. Sometimes it is obvious to everyone but your aged relative that it is unsafe for him to drive, but he may resist any attempt by the family to make him give up the pleasure and independence that driving provide. License laws vary in different states, but in some states an anonymous notification to the police or the Department of Motor Vehicles will cause the authority to call the elderly person in for a driving test. A feeble stroke patient of mine, highly indignant at being told by his family that he should not drive, was sufficiently disturbed at the idea of taking a test that he gave up driving voluntarily. He never knew that a relative had called the authorities.

Quick or immediate solutions to problems that arise are not to be counted on. Inevitably there will be wounded feelings. Uncle George will be despondent because of his bereavement and in having to give up the home he had shared with his wife for fifty years. Daughter-in-law will be exasperated when Grandmother pointedly remarks on the tear in Junior's shirt.

There is a time to weep and a time to laugh, as the

Preacher says in Ecclesiastes, and each has its place in the order of things. If Grandmother is upset for no apparent reason, suggest firmly but lovingly that company is expected and perhaps she should go to her room and get ready. Surely she wants to look nice for the people soon to appear.

Father should never let himself be caught in the middle. He and Mother should present a united front before others in any dispute, even though in private they may have to compromise on a different decision.

A frequent cause of conflict in the early period is the assumption by Mother, who is tired anyway, that Grandmother has moved in to be a servant in the house. If Grandmother is able to manage a house she should not be living with her descendants except as an act of mercy on her part when an invalid requires her care.

Most elderly relatives, if they are reasonably healthy and competent, are glad to baby-sit sometimes, but this willingness should not be imposed upon. The responsibility may worry them, or they may take advantage of the chance to disrupt established discipline.

Children and adolescents need attention, and within limits it is difficult to give them too much. This is where an elderly relative can be a great blessing if she can help with homework or mending; however, if she uses ill-temper, petulance, and spite to get attention, she should be requested to go to the crying room until the mood has passed.

People living together should learn to "forget" conveniently. Crises can often be steered into oblivion in a matter of an hour. What seems like a crisis in the making can often be averted when a clever daughter takes off for a breath of air or when Grandmother retires to her room for that daytime TV series. Don't let anyone continue to pout—settle the problem, or sidestep it and begin anew.

Usually after a period of several weeks, things will

have settled into a routine in which most people can live in comfortable equanimity.

The advice in this chapter can be summarized by some do's and don'ts.

DO:

Maintain a routine.

Have an acknowledged head of the house.

Have Dad and Mother stick together, in dealing with the grandparent as well as in disciplining the children.

Have regular jobs for elderly folk within the limits of their physical powers.

Have children treat grandparents with kindness and respect.

See that all adults have regular periods of rest and relaxation. This is essential for maintenance of physical and emotional health. Father and Mother should arrange to get out together from time to time.

Encourage happiness and laughter. Few people remain sad when others are cheerful.

See that the various members of the family express thanks often, especially to Mother and Grandmother.

DON'T:

Out of misplaced respect, allow Grandmother to become the boss of the house.

Let bitterness or resentment smolder. Each hour is a good time to start over.

Make an old person a body servant, doing all the chores.

Do things only out of a sense of duty and determination. Grim, unsmiling demeanor robs life of all gladness.

Neglect young children while Uncle Bill gets more than his share of attention.

Offend anyone's sense of fair play and decency.

# ❦ 16 ❦

# Patient and Doctor

Many books have been written on the relationship between doctor and patient, but the role of physician is too often not understood. Some families expect the doctor to be all things to all people at all times and become disillusioned when the physician fails to live up to this impossible demand. This chapter deals with what can reasonably be expected of a physician and the courtesy he should be able to expect from patients and their families.

Physicians too have their failings and personal problems and limitations. They too need reassurance, comfort, and understanding. In choosing a doctor, the patient and the family should consider the following: First, *is he able?* Second, *is he available?* Last, *is he affable?* These questions were first asked, so far as I know, by Horace Cotten in *Medical Economics.*

If a physician is able, he is perceptive; he is willing to take time to distinguish between what is serious and what is of minor importance. Whether or not he has a warm personality, he has good judgment and can inspire confidence.

Today physicians, male and female, are usually well trained. Some are less secure than others and place more reliance on tests and hospitals. Generally speaking, younger physicians are more given to heroic treatment and elaborate testing than are older practitioners. This distinction could be of some help in choosing a suitable physician. Even so, the hospital-testing physician could be criticized for causing too much commotion; the one who relies on his own experience and judgment with a degree of diffidence could be accused of not caring. In my own practice I have learned to sense the needs of the family, but generally to avoid collecting useless data and hauling feeble old people to strange hospitals.

In general, leave it to the family doctor to decide when a consultation with a specialist is needed. The layman does not know the difference between surgical and nonsurgical kidney disease, for example. It is exhausting and time-consuming for the doctor to have to explain the difference between what a *urologist* (kidney specialist) treats and what is treated by a generalist or internist, or, in connection with nervous disorders, the difference between a *neurological surgeon* and a *neurologist*. Every sick woman does not need a *gynecologist* (a specialist in female organs); an elderly woman who wets the bed may need a gynecologist, but she may instead need a urologist, or a neurologist, or she may need all three.

Every person with heart trouble does not need a heart specialist (*cardiologist*); everyone with a digestive problem does not need a stomach specialist (*gastroenterologist*); everyone with a skin rash does not need a skin specialist (*dermatologist*). Joint specialists (*orthopedic surgeons*) don't treat the usual cases of arthritis; they are surgeons, and most joints don't need surgery. Head specialists or ear, nose, and throat doctors (*otorhinolaryngologists*) don't treat the usual causes of headache or ear disorders which may be due to faulty circulation.

A *gerontologist* is a specialist in aging and its problems. A *geriatrician* specializes in diseases of old age. These specialists have overlapping functions, which are not well defined except in a few research centers.

Assure your physician that if he needs a consultant, the family will accept his judgment, but leave the decision to him. Don't hold him responsible for the time the consultant will appear and don't expect him necessarily to follow the line of treatment the consultant suggests.

An eye specialist (*ophthalmologist*) once prescribed a medicine which nauseated my patient; he then prescribed another medicine to counteract the nausea and told her to continue to take both. After a month I persuaded her that she could get along very well without either, and so she did.

Most specialists treat symptoms or organs. Generalists treat people.

In the matter of a physician's availability, people often expect more than is possible under present-day conditions. Some think the physician should be on the spot for every ache or pain. How often have I left the office, driven through city traffic, deprived someone else of my services, only to find that an old lady's "gas on the stomach" was simply caused by overeating. After such experiences it is not surprising that physicians are reluctant to make house calls, but the medical profession is rightly criticized for the increasing tendency to refuse to supply home service under any circumstances. In most situations, however, a physician's availability can be fairly judged by his willingness to see a patient in his office or hospital in an emergency, to give calming reassurance by telephone, or to help to locate another doctor for the patient.

When a doctor is at home he is usually pretty weary. He shouldn't be called from a meal or slumber about a cold, a stubbed toe, or other trivial indisposition.

Accept substitutes gladly in emergencies. An old lady patient of mine nearly died of pneumonia because she would not see a substitute when I was out of town for ten days. Now that group practices are largely replacing solo practitioners, this problem is less important.

Discuss your physician's availability with him. Learn what you can expect from him. Get his advice on procedure in case of a real emergency when he is not available; do not resent the fact that he may not always be on tap. He probably is with someone else, and may have several emergencies awaiting him. If the patient is being treated at a clinic, find out what emergency facilities are available.

How often should an old person see his physician? This can be answered by saying, "As often as is necessary to keep the doctor familiar with the general condition of the patient, and often enough for the patient to know this." Some physicians would prefer to see the patient for ten minutes once a week; others for sixty minutes once a year. Let the doctor decide, but be sure to notify him when there is some new development in the patient's condition.

Affability is a relative matter, and certainly less important than ability and availability. You hear these days that the doctor doesn't smile much, or seems brusk and bossy. While no one likes dealing with a grouch, either as patient or physician, some physicians can say more with a grunt and a shrug than the more loquacious doctors can put into words. Allow for individual variations in personality. Doctors are people, and sometimes they are more tired, hurried, or worried than at other times. Don't expect the doctor always to be larger than life; Christ himself showed irritation on several occasions.

Being human, doctors respond to small courtesies like anyone else. I well remember from private practice thoughtful gestures and small offerings such as a jar of damson preserves, a fresh-caught fish, and other treats that people brought to me, above and beyond paying their bills. Don't offer anything that would tend to obligate the physician. He is well paid. He is probably most grateful for words of appreciation and respect for his time.

A physician should not be required to give a detailed explanation of the patient's condition to every member of the family. This creates confusion and anxiety, causes misunderstandings within the family, and above all wastes the time of the physician. One person in the family should be delegated to get medical reports and circulate them among the other members of the family. This one-delegate plan should prevail at home, at the hospital, at the doctor's office, or on the telephone—regardless of how ill the patient may be.

Do not hold the doctor responsible for the type of hospital accommodation or the efficiency of the nursing service. The time has long since passed when doctors had the final say in the operation of most hospitals.

Unfortunately, some patients try to buy what is not available at any price: a private room, at times even a hospital bed, preferential treatment, all sorts of special attention from the physician.

Unfortunately, also, there are a few physicians who build themselves up by collecting patients they consider important and whose care is proportional to the big shot's reputation.

The true physician is interested in all kinds of people, young and old, rich and poor, educated and ignorant, the high and mighty, and the meek and lowly. He gives his best knowledge and attention to all who need it and often with an extra measure of patience for the old.

People sometimes ask how to decide whether they should consider changing doctors. Actually, there are very few good reasons for such a change. In considering the possibility, you should realize that a replacement for your aged relative's regular doctor may not be easy to find; today there are more people needing care than there are doctors seeking patients. With elderly people, you should be aware that you may not be able to try on doctors as you try on a new hat.

Do not "try on" a doctor because his patients ascribe magic powers to him that other doctors do not have: he probably will be unsuccessful in treating your grandparent and so disappoint the whole family. Besides, in finding a physician, the qualities to look for should be general ability and faithfulness over the long pull.

When I started practice I was appalled by the number of people who turned from the physician who had treated them for years because they thought I would be more pliable and easily exploited. Don't change physicians when the one you have is self-assured enough to say no on occasion.

Don't reject a physician because he has come to understand what an old reprobate your Uncle Timothy really is. Some people don't want understanding; they merely want medical approval for their general cussedness. If the doctor will put up with Uncle Timothy, don't change. The next one would find him out sooner or later.

Don't change doctors when your aged relative is angry or distraught. Let him cool off. Wait a day or two. Then, if you think a change is in order, say to the doctor. "Dr. Jones, we're discouraged and we guess you are too. Thank you for all you've done, but we believe we'll try a change of doctors." Do not name the replacement.

Do not allow people who have not been on the scene to make the decisions. Once I salvaged a poor old lady by heroic though reasonable effort. Then her eldest daughter arrived at the sickbed from a thousand miles away and summarily dismissed me in favor of her own preferred physician. This was not only unfair to me but very upsetting to the helpless old woman who had to adjust to a new personality and a different course of treatment.

Do not dismiss a physician because your second guess was better than his first. Physicians, politicians, and athletic coaches are always being second-guessed. Some relatives, never wrong in their own eyes, can always tell when a cold will develop into pneumonia, when an infection will be unresponsive to penicillin but responsive to tetracycline, whether a swelling is cancerous or benign. If the doctor has the second guess, he too is at an advantage; few doctors are impressed with the superior wisdom which second-guessers claim.

A physician may occasionally ask to be relieved of a case. This usually occurs when he has been involved with family complications of the kind described here and seems to get nowhere in spite of his best efforts. He should be allowed to withdraw without bitterness.

The only good reasons for asking a physician to withdraw are: if he repeatedly fails to do what he promises he will do; if he does not show proper concern for the patient; or if he plainly lacks the dignity, propriety, and ordinary competence of a doctor.

## ⁊ 17 ⁊

# When to Telephone the Doctor

Legitimate uses of the telephone are to save time and to relieve anxiety. I believe that most physicians would cheerfully find these uses acceptable. When the telephone is used inconsiderately, or as a social device, it can become a nuisance to the doctor and he may react accordingly. This inevitably leads to misunderstanding.

Patients and their families should remember that most physicians in private practice have more duties than they can accomplish comfortably. Unnecessary calls are annoying as well as time-consuming. I was once called away from a patient in my office by another elderly woman whose question was, "Doctor, am I allowed to eat a mango? It isn't on my list."

If the physician, in making out a prescription, indicates whether or not it may be refilled, calls can be avoided. Patients should not insist on talking with the doctor personally when his nurse is able to answer the question about procedure, change of appointment, the result of a laboratory test, or any other routine matter relating to medical care.

Among the calls that are most trying to the doctor is

the demand for a full explanation of the patient's condition and the course of treatment—usually on a weekend, a
holiday, at the doctor's home, or during the busiest time of
day. A typical call comes from the daughter from out of
town, who arrives to find Mama looking worse than she had
the previous summer. The explanation of the in-town sister
that Mama is getting older and feebler does not suffice; the
doctor must be apprised of the observation from out of town,
called to account for his shortcomings, and ordered to make
immediate amends for his supposed neglect.

The various members of the family should avoid calling
the doctor and repeating the same questions. By the time the
doctor has explained coronary thrombosis to Mary, Sue,
Jane, and Joe individually he may rebel when the fifth member of the family demands a complete definition and prognosis.

If the doctor has given full instructions to Mary, Sue, or
Joe with prescriptions, diet, special instructions, and a future
appointment, he resents having another family member call
and ask what was said thirty minutes ago.

I know that many telephone calls are made out of
sincere concern for the patient. Most doctors appreciate
this; they merely want some of the same consideration
shown them.

As a private practitioner I appreciated the kindness of
people and their concern for my welfare. At times it seemed
that people would do anything in the world for me except
leave me alone. Like all human beings, doctors want to
feel they are needed, but they also need to eat a meal, to
have a leisure moment, or a night of uninterrupted sleep.

Too often people call the doctor to complain about
things over which he has no control. He cannot do anything
about an unruly neighbor in the hospital bed next to his

patient. He cannot accomplish any more than a hall nurse in getting another accommodation.

It is an imposition to telephone a doctor to prescribe for an ache or a cold in a patient he has never seen. In such instances the doctor also is often expected to call a druggist for a medicine which could be purchased over the counter.

No doctor likes to be called at night for things that can be managed equally well during the day. If you call the doctor and don't get an immediate answer, don't be surprised. A doctor who receives forty calls and sees twenty or more patients in his office a day is bound to have conflicts. The patients in his waiting room have the first right to the doctor's time, and it is not fair to take the time they are paying for when the telephone matter can be attended to later. Most physicians conscientiously try to return all calls at the end of the day, if not before.

The doctor expects and appreciates a call if he requests it to learn about the patient's condition or the results of a treatment. He may ask to be called at a certain time of day which he reserves for the telephone. He expects to be called in case of a real emergency. He may also want to be consulted if the patient develops a persistent symptom that cannot wait until the next visit.

Ask the doctor what his attitude toward telephone calls is; he probably can give you some instructions.

In general, remember that the doctor is busier than most people realize. Put yourself in his position and multiply your call by forty. Make sure that the call is necessary.

# ❦ 18 ❧

# Appointment with the Doctor

What, in general, should be accomplished by a visit to the doctor's office?

When a physician is assuming overall care of an old person, he should be given basic information about his patient. He will probably want to make a thorough examination, including blood tests for anemia, infections, or other blood disorders; he will want to check the urine for signs of kidney disorders or diabetes; he may have good reasons for other tests which he should explain briefly.

Grandmother may be reluctant to undress for a physical examination, but it is important that the physician have a basis for comparison; often the significance of a finding will not be obvious until sometime later.

This basic physical appraisal may be accomplished in one or several visits; let the doctor decide.

After doctor and patient become acquainted with each other and questions regarding fees, availability, and emergency care have been satisfactorily answered, the doctor-patient relationship has truly begun.

Unfortunately, patients or their relatives sometimes expect treatment for every symptom during an appointment. The doctor will usually ask questions about important symptoms, but the elderly person should not be encouraged to go into great detail. How often, on asking, "Do you have a good appetite?" have I had to hear a review of a whole day's menu down to the texture of the toast and the fruit in the fritters.

A good question to ask is: "Doctor, is such-and-such important?" His answer possibly can give reassurance without going into a discourse on why a little giddiness or a tingling in the hands is usually nothing to cause alarm.

Make a list of these "Is it important?" questions, rather than worrying or telephoning. In a calm moment you can cross out most of them. The doctor will be much more patient and will have more time to spend with the patient than if you were to ask, for example, "Doctor, why does Mama open her mouth when she sleeps?" (The list of questions can be endless and there are no real answers that would be important in any case.)

A word about clothing for the visit to the doctor is in order. Some dear old ladies don't get out often, and when they do they are corseted, brassiered, underclothed, and bundled up in such a way as to frustrate a harried, hurried doctor who would like to examine a patient without having to unravel a cocoon. Preferred above all is loose-fitting clothing which can be easily pushed aside or removed.

These days most doctors' offices can be entered without undue exposure, even in slippers and dressing gowns.

If the chest is the area to be checked, a single garment makes it easy. A woman can wear a blouse and slip out of shoulder straps quickly without fully undressing, if foresight is used. A man can wear a short-sleeved shirt if only blood pressure needs to be checked.

Nearly every doctor has a bookkeeper or secretary who

can manage business details. Ask her the questions about payment or insurance forms. The doctor is not the one to ask unless his aides have failed to give satisfaction.

The doctor cannot personally give every treatment or do every test. He probably has in his employ a technician who can give an injection or take an X ray or a heart tracing (electrocardiogram) with unquestionable skill.

By all means keep appointments on time, and where possible make them well in advance. Then you can expect the doctor to be prompt and reasonably patient, unless unusual circumstances arise. If he is not, you have good ground for complaint.

The time of waiting can be profitably used. If the patient is to have weight and temperature checked, an aide can do this before the doctor even knows of the patient's arrival. A diabetic should always be ready with a freshly filled bottle of urine or a full bladder.

On going to the doctor it is a good plan for the elderly person to take all medicines with him. Thus the doctor can keep adequate records, and the patient is protected from having too many prescriptions. I have been appalled at the amount of medicine some people take, and for this the doctor will have to assume part of the responsibility. Patients, families, and physicians should try to limit the quantity of medicine consumed. Generally if a person gets no benefit from three or four medicines, fourteen won't improve matters.

Almost any medicine will occasionally have a bad reaction. If a new medicine causes nausea it will do no harm to skip a dose and call the doctor in the morning. Patients and their families—and even doctors—can sometimes confuse the effects of a drug with the condition under treatment. Leave off a dose or two and check later. In this situation the doctor will know what to advise.

The doctor is not bound to follow any treatment Grandfather may have had in the past, even though it may have seemed to help. Penicillin shots have killed people; liver extract confuses the doctor; B$_{12}$ isn't a cure-all; hormones generally are not helpful for overweight; garlic doesn't relieve high blood pressure; watermelon seeds for kidney trouble is ridiculous; sassafras isn't the best thing going for colds; honey and vinegar never cured arthritis . . . I could go on and on with a recital of futile nostrums.

The wise doctor will not ridicule a treatment he disapproves of; just don't ask him to continue it.

In home visits the same general rules apply. The doctor may reserve the right to make routine home visits at his convenience when it is not a matter of urgency. Try to save his time. If Uncle George has hemorrhoids, urge him to lie down before the doctor arrives; hemorrhoids cannot be examined when a person is sitting on them. If a mole on the back is to be investigated, have Aunt Tillie sit up if possible. These are small things, but they can be of great help to both patient and doctor.

# ❧ 19 ❧

# It Takes All Kinds

I have mentioned that adjustments will have to be made in the home after the elderly person moves in. To a great extent these are psychological adjustments that all generations must make.

Now I want to consider certain nervous reactions which are much more prevalent or more pronounced in the elderly. I shall list them first and then discuss them a little more fully in this and the following chapters: complaining; depression and anxiety; fault-finding; petulance; hostility; forgetfulness; self-righteousness; authoritarianism.

First let me say that I have found many sweet, cheerful, and grateful old people who rarely manifest any of these traits. The personality of an elderly person is conditioned in large measure by his outlook early in life. Growing old does not make a sweet person out of a grouch; it does not make a lover of mankind out of a hostile person. The grouch becomes even grouchier and the hateful all the more so.

A complaining old person usually has not had to cope with much discomfort in the past. Often something new and fearful has entered into the experience of septuagenarians.

Aside from specific diseases, the complaints are so numerous and so unusual and frequently so trivial that they cannot be accounted for except as a symptom of waning strength.

Working from the head down, an elderly man may complain of dizziness, ringing in the ears, spots before the eyes, blurred vision, stopped-up ears, dry mouth, throbbing in the temples, "hearing the heart beat," stiffness in the neck, racing heart, inability to take a deep breath, numbness in the fingers, various forms of indigestion, constipation, cold feet, aching in the joints, and other sensations too vague to name.

All these symptoms can be caused by nervous tension or by sitting or lying a long time in an awkward, strained position. Some will be discussed later in the appropriate chapters. One must remember that, as old people hear of the death of friends and relatives, they become more conscious of what the future holds in store for them and interpret their symptoms in this light. The pulse at the temple beating against the pillow becomes a sign of heart trouble. The dry mouth that results from sleeping with the mouth open is translated as indicating diabetes. The giddiness that comes from arthritis at the upper part of the spine is interpreted as a sign of impending stroke. The heart skip can mean only a heart attack.

Inability to draw a deep, satisfying breath in a cramped position, or as often as one cares to sigh, in the mind of the fearful becomes a warning of heart or lung trouble. People who gulp air in an effort to belch may become bloated and feel that they have a dangerous stomach ailment. Numbness in the hands after prolonged lying or sitting they may consider a sign of "poor circulation" or a developing apoplexy. Aches in certain joints may be due to sitting or lying in a cramped position. None of these symptoms is serious unless the patient's condition is clearly becoming worse by the hour. Wait until there is some more urgent reason to call the doctor, and then ask about these troubling sensations.

The preceding are only a few of the physical ailments people complain about. Many old people do have serious physical disorders and these will presently be discussed. The point I make here is that many complaints are *not* serious. Simple remedies, such as aspirin or one of its substitutes, a heating pad, a warm bath, or a gentle massage will often relieve the condition. Minor indispositions will sometimes disappear if the sufferer is given something to occupy his mind or time, thus diverting his attention.

Do not take every little symptom seriously. Stay calm. Assure the complainer that death is not imminent.

I remember being called at three in the morning to an elderly patient who, believing himself at his final hour, was admonishing his various descendants: "John, you quit drinking! Hubert, you take care of your mother! Mary, you ought to get married again." The whole family had panicked because Father had a stomachache that proved to be due to a forbidden dill pickle.

Look for the simple and the obvious before calling for help. Serious symptoms do not allow themselves to be ignored or forgotten.

Have Grandfather examined occasionally, but do not call for emergency treatment for trivialities.

# ❧ 20 ❧

# Depressed or Anxious Old People

The word "depression" has a technical meaning for the doctor, which the patient's family often does not understand. Simply put, a depression is a state of mind in which a person's outlook on life becomes excessively gloomy, when he lapses into a panic due to fear, or when he develops physical symptoms as a reflection of excessive despair or apprehension. The depressed patient may not complain of pain. He may be seen as a slowly responding, silent, bent-over figure seeking to be alone. He may reply haltingly to questions, become untidy in his habits, and eat sparsely. Questioned, he will answer in a few words. He will show little or no interest in his surroundings and present the semblance of deep despair. If he can be engaged in conversation at all, he is likely to show a negative outlook. "No," he may say, "it is not a nice day." For him the sky is gloomy, the food is tasteless, the chair is uncomfortable, the shoe does not fit, and so on.

Such a person may also show marked symptoms of anxiety. This anxiety may be an obsessive concern about money, health, insurance. It may be undue concern about

71

the comings and goings of relatives. It may result from changed surroundings, a different atmosphere. The anxiety or panic is always out of proportion to the circumstances.

When such anxiety or agitation is combined with many of the features of the purely depressed patient, the person is said to have an *agitated depression.*

The danger of depression in a fairly vigorous person is that it may sometimes lead to suicide. Drugs are available that can help to counteract the depressed or agitated state, although seldom is the condition really cured in the very old. Do not try to diagnose these conditions yourself. We all get the blues. A true depression is best diagnosed by a physician.

People can be very anxious yet show no outward evidence of depression. These elderly individuals remain alert—too alert. They are deeply troubled about themselves, their surroundings, other people, and their bodily symptoms. They are apt to pace back and forth, to sleep poorly, and to intrude in things which do not concern them. Indeed, they seem to be looking for trouble. They simply cannot relax. The anxious elderly patient does not differ greatly from an anxious youngster who can usually manufacture a crisis if he doesn't find one already present.

Modern drugs, as I have indicated, can often relieve anxiety to a great extent, but remember that anxiety is no emergency in itself. Too many times I have been called out at night because "Mama is nervous." Once I was called because "Dad has the fidgets"—as accurate a diagnosis as I myself could have made after getting out of bed, dressing, driving five miles, and elbowing my way through a houseful of cousins, nieces, sons, and daughters to the old man's bedside for a midnight examination—totally unnecessary.

Usually calm solicitude, a warm bath, and a bit of firmness will help an old person overcome nervous anxiety. Such statements as, "Dad, I'm sorry you're so nervous, but it's nothing serious. Let me rub your back," will help. Anxiety is often relieved by "the laying on of hands." Human beings respond to touch when they need comforting. A massage, a heating pad, a warm bath, coupled with a few comforting words, are often all that is needed to relax the patient. For suggestions on dealing with seriously disturbed people, see Chapter 34.

# ❦ 21 ❦

# Fault-finding, Petulance, and Hostility

These traits are considered together because they often occur in the same person. This is the sort of individual who throughout his entire life has been motivated by the desire to find fault and who is sustained by grouchiness. Such unfortunate people are difficult even during their best years and in old age they can only be handled with firmness and the utmost patience.

For them nothing is satisfactory. The food is poor, the bed is uncomfortable, the doctor is a veterinarian, the medicine gives no relief, and "no one does anything for me." They complain about mechanical aids which have been properly fitted and checked and are in good working order. Since glasses are less satisfactory than normal vision, dentures never work as well as teeth, hearing aids are cumbersome, a truss, though necessary, is bound to be a nuisance, these complaints also are only an expression of an unrealistic attitude. Sometimes one can suggest, "Grandfather, why don't you take out your teeth for a while?" but if Grandfather is a complainer he will probably go on complaining.

Such people are also likely to be troublemakers. When Grandfather is living with John, he will tell daughter Jane on her visits that he is neglected and mistreated, but if he moves to Jane's house, he will vituperate against her and threaten to cut her out of his will.

All this talk is an attention-getting device and should be recognized as such. Try responding to a tirade with such statements as "Dad, I'm sorry you're not comfortable, but we are doing the best we can," or "Aunt Phyllis, we love you very much, but we don't love that kind of talk."

If reasoning proves useless, simply saying, "Mom, you're upset now and I'm going to leave you alone until you can be nice," and departing for a while, will enforce a little discipline.

Some individuals become so hostile that they throw dishes or strike out with walking canes. Such violent outbursts are comparable to children's temper tantrums. Tranquilizers in sufficient doses sometimes help to put the old person into a calmer and more reasonable state of mind.

In dealing with petulance and hostility, never be provoked into a yelling contest. Don't descend to argument with an aged relative who is trying to call attention to himself. Never strike back with words. Appear to be listening but do not knuckle under. As soon as the petulance, fault-finding, and hostility have had their inning, start on something pleasant and ignore the spat.

Following this course requires great patience, practice, and understanding. Do not be dismayed if you fall short of perfection in dealing with this kind of individual. Take frequent outings and get adequate rest—you'll need it to cope with the general cussedness of the self-centered, fault-finding, aging member of the family.

# ❧ 22 ❧

# Forgetfulness

More disturbing than other nervous symptoms is failing memory. A fairly vigorous elderly person may at times become extremely absent-minded.

The failing memory may manifest itself according to a pattern or may show no pattern whatever. Familiar routines may be forgotten. An elderly person may forget to wash her face or put on her stockings. Uncle Bill may forget that he's already had his morning meal and demand, "Doesn't this house serve breakfast?"

It is characteristic of this condition that recent events are forgotten but past events can be remembered in the minutest detail, although the details may not be entirely accurate.

Forgetfulness in the aged is often ascribed to narrowing of the blood channels, although younger people with this condition usually have no impairment of memory. Sometimes the doctor will prescribe something to help the circulation, but such remedies are not very effective.

Failing memory does not mean that a stroke is imminent, as some people believe, even though strokes can occur in aging people with poor memories.

Do not make a big fuss about an old person's failing memory. He is more aware of it than you are. It can't be helped, and calling attention to it repeatedly only results in further confusion.

If poor memory causes great anxiety or concern in the patient, the condition can become aggravated. If the family shows alarm, the anxiety will probably increase, and the forgetfulness as well. This is the time for tranquilizers all around.

# 23

# Self-Righteous and Authoritarian Old People

I sometimes think that the greatest family strife is caused by the self-righteous and authoritarian elderly matron. This is usually a woman who has raised her family with an iron hand. She has become a self-acknowledged expert on conduct. She does not hesitate to insist on her own way of doing things. She is apt to be an authority on the management of grandchildren and is critical of disciplinary measures by parents. If she sees a button missing she can't simply sew it on but must berate daughter because it wasn't sewed on previously.

She is apt to be critical of others' taste in pictures or music. She seems to tell herself that she has never entertained an impure thought and she is most uncharitable to all who do not agree with her, criticizing clothes, manners, speech, and even facial expressions.

An authoritarian person is a self-appointed expert on anything. Ask such an authority a simple question and you are in for a dissertation. Self-righteous people are often those who have been brought up with strict religious precepts which they use to lord it over the sinners.

There is no specific treatment that will change such natures, but indulgent good humor can often avoid hard feelings. One might end needless repetition by saying, "Aunt Mary, I have to go now to pick up the children." Don't argue: you can't win!

# ❧ 24 ❧

# Physical Symptoms:
# Disorder of Vision, Hearing,
# Smell, and Taste

We have discussed common behavior problems in the aged. Now let us turn our attention to physical symptoms related to the eyes, ears, nose, and tongue.

By far the most common eye disease is *cataract*. This is clouding of the lens, so that things may appear blurred, particularly at a distance. If the eyes are otherwise healthy, cataract removal is successful in about 90 to 95 percent of cases.

For most old people there is much anxiety about vision and surgery, which is relatively simple, but the elderly become apprehensive about the possibility of blindness; they need strong moral support with an impending cataract operation. The physician will usually prescribe a tranquilizer if the patient shows considerable agitation.

Although operations are usually successful, concomitant eye disease may prevent a good result following extraction of cataracts. There is no great shock to the body, and patients in their nineties have done well after cataract surgery. However, they may be discouraged because good results are slow in coming. The eye requires several weeks to heal, and then proper glasses must be fitted. During this waiting period your relative may show evidence of misgiving and despondency; if so, reassurance and a mild sedative are in order. Do all you can to overcome his alarm.

Another eye ailment that occurs is excessive dryness due to insufficient flow of moisture from the tear glands. The eyelids may become inflamed and turned out. There may be blind spots or other visual disturbances. These are not emergencies but should be treated by an eye physician, who will also check for *glaucoma* which can do serious harm if left untreated.

In the event of an eye operation, elderly patients may lose track of place, time, and persons' identity during the period while the eyes are bandaged. This should not distress you; it usually clears up promptly once the person can see, even partially.

If vision changes rapidly from week to week, diabetes should be suspected. Often new glasses have been obtained, only to become inadequate when vision fails as a result of diabetes. It would be a good idea to have the urine checked for sugar before new glasses are prescribed. Vision is often vastly improved when the diabetic condition is kept under control.

A considerable number of old people develop a very keen sense of smell and can detect odors that others are unaware of. This is due, in most instances, to the extreme self-consciousness present in many nervous people.

You will sometimes hear the complaints of failing sense of taste, or a bitter taste, a sour taste, or a dry tongue. Many of these changes in taste perception are caused by breathing through the mouth. In other instances there is faulty digestion and a person will belch or be conscious of an unpleasant odor from the stomach. When this occurs it is usually more obvious and troublesome to the patient than to anyone else, although unpleasant breath is occasionally noted by others. Mints or enzyme medications may be prescribed; these will help occasionally. Certain medicines cause dryness of the mouth or a bitter taste; among these are digitalis, belladonna-like drugs, and various medications for rheumatic disorders.

In the old, hearing may become impaired, and this is mostly due to the deterioration of the auditory nerves; however, hearing can sometimes be improved by washing out the accumulated wax. Elderly people can be helped with hearing aids. Deafness should be checked by an ear specialist, who can often alleviate the condition.

The inner ear helps in maintaining the sense of balance; this part of the ear may be affected by poor circulation or other conditions still not thoroughly understood, so that a person becomes dizzy, nauseated, and unable to stand. This condition is called *Ménière's syndrome* and can be disabling, though it is usually not serious. It is more apt to occur with sudden changes of position or when the patient is upset. Medicines can alleviate the symptoms to some extent.

# { 25 }

# Heart and Lung Symptoms

Cough, pain in the chest, and shortness of breath are the usual symptoms of heart or lung disorders. However, do not jump to the conclusion that all coughs, chest pains, and shortness of breath are signs of danger.

Many older people, particularly those with a lifetime smoking habit, have a rattle in the chest that causes little impairment of health. A change in the character of the cough, or any expectoration of yellowish or greenish mucus, could be a sign of complication, and then a physician should be consulted.

A few elderly people with early weakening of the heart will have blood dammed back into the lungs and so develop a hacking cough, usually associated with shortness of breath. These symptoms should be called to the doctor's attention, although they do not necessarily indicate an emergency and respond readily to treatment.

Shortness of breath and undue fatigue from routine activity probably indicate *congestive heart failure*. The pulse may race and the patient may be more comfortable sitting than lying. Treatment for this condition should not be delayed.

Associated with shortness of breath there may be swelling of the legs and ankles, particularly when a person has been sitting long in one position. This condition is called *edema* or *dropsy* and is due to accumulation of body salt and water in the lower limbs.

People with sound hearts will sometimes develop edema if the skin is loose and they remain inactive. For the same reason, shoes may become tight on a long drive; such edema is no indication of disease.

There are many types of chest pain, most of which are not serious. If one can explore on the chest and find a tender spot, the pain is most likely not serious. If pain is aggravated by reaching, stooping, or bending, it is probably not serious. Heart pain is usually indicated by a tightness across the breast which may extend to neck or shoulder. If this usually follows exertion and is relieved within a couple of minutes by rest, the probable cause is *angina pectoris*, which requires medical supervision, especially if attacks become more frequent or severe.

If a pain of this kind occurs abruptly and is attended by nausea, pallor, and sweating, it could be due to *coronary thrombosis* and demands prompt medical attention.

Another type of acute heart condition is indicated by the onset of severe shortness of breath, coughing, and expectoration of foamy fluid. The attack frequently comes on when the patient is lying on his back. Propping him up in a chair may give relief, but medical attention should be obtained promptly. The patient may be covered with perspiration, accompanied by pallor and bluish lips. This is a real emergency, a condition termed *acute pulmonary edema*.

Heart emergencies can often be prevented by appropriate treatment. Once treatment is started, do not allow medicine to be stopped except under medical supervision. Many elderly people have had severe emergencies because they have neglected to take their digitalis.

These are some of the more usual heart symptoms. All need regular medical attention, but often the condition can be controlled for years, with the patient remaining in relatively good health.

*Pneumonia* in the aged is a danger, particularly with heart trouble. Usually there will be a hacking cough and extreme weakness with fever. Fever, however, is not a reliable sign in the very old.

Influenza seldom kills anyone except the very old. Flu vaccine each fall gives protection against some 70 percent of the prevalent flu viruses. It is an advisable precaution for most old people.

Many elderly people, frequently the inveterate smokers, develop *asthma, bronchitis,* and *emphysema,* which usually go together. They wheeze in breathing, are subject to cold complications, and suffer from shortness of breath. Such patients may have a bluish skin or lips. They may get along fairly well until they get a cold, and then they have difficulty in breathing.

Ordinarily, physicians prescribe something to keep down complications of colds. Since most have a great deal of thick phlegm in the windpipes, it is helpful for them to have *postural drainage.* This maneuver entails lying across the bed, belly down, lowering the head almost to the floor, and coughing. A weak patient can be treated by putting several pillows under the abdomen while he lies on the bed. This allows the mucus to flow downward, so to speak, and helps to relieve the obstruction in the bronchial tubes. Sputum can be coughed onto several layers of old newspapers which are then burned, or the patient can spit into a pan, which may be less trouble.

## ❧ 26 ❧

# Symptoms of Digestive Trouble

Obviously this book cannot include a detailed description of all symptoms. Only the more dangerous and prevalent disorders will be listed.

The following digestive symptoms should serve as guidance to good management.

1. Simple *indigestion*, manifested by bloating, belching, bad taste in the mouth, coated tongue, and sour stomach, is most often due to simple nervousness. It may be caused by overseasoned food, and in patients far advanced in age it may be caused by a deficiency in the digestive juices. Little more than tranquil living and a mild but appetizing diet are required.

2. Persistent burning or boring pain in the upper or mid-abdomen, which is relieved by soda or another antacid or by eating, may be due to a *peptic ulcer* which can be diagnosed with certainty only by X ray.

3. Nausea and vomiting, if persistent, always demand X-ray study. Infrequent nausea due to intolerance of food or some virus should cause no alarm.

4. Tarry stools—yes, as black as tar—indicate bleeding

from high up in the digestive tract, and are most often due to an ulcer. This is a serious symptom and demands prompt attention. However, tarry stools may be caused by commercial digestive aids containing bismuth, and also by fresh meat.

5. Severe pains in the stomach which persist, at times better and then worse, can result from a number of causes, but if they do not disappear in an hour or two probably need medical attention. The cause may be a "locked bowel" or, as doctors say, an *intestinal obstruction*.

6. Severe, prolonged bloating of the abdomen, especially if accompanied by colicky pain, demands a doctor's care.

7. A painful swelling in the groin may indicate a trapped hernia. If the swelling does not go away on lying down, it may demand immediate medical treatment. Hernia should be attended to before it becomes trapped, by fitting with a truss or by surgery.

8. Severe or recurring pain in the region of the right lower ribs may indicate gall bladder or liver disease and likewise calls for medical attention. If a person has a very dark urine or a yellow skin color, he has *jaundice*, and is apt to have a stone in one of the bile tubes.

9. *Constipation* may be a stubborn problem, particularly if the patient is in bed most of the time. Most old people require some bowel aid, but harsh laxatives should be avoided. Mineral oil, about an ounce a day, will help to avoid a painful condition called a *fecal impaction*, which is a hard, puttylike accumulation of waste material in the rectum. An impaction can be relieved only by repeated enemas, purges, and suppositories. It is best to guard against this condition, which, though not serious, is painful.

10. Intermittent soreness, sometimes rather acute, usually in the lower sides of the abdomen, may be due to inflamed little pockets in the bowel called diverticuli; the condition is known as *diverticulitis*. Diagnosis is made with

certainty only by X ray, but the condition is usually not serious and relief occurs with simple medication. On rare occasions complications may require surgery.

11. Bleeding from the rectum usually is from enlarged veins called hemorrhoids which have become torn, but such bleeding can also be a sign of more serious trouble, including cancer.

Cancer and appendicitis have not been mentioned because the symptoms are not easily described. The best guard against serious disease is a periodic check. Do not wait until midnight or a Sunday before checking persistent symptoms.

As in any disease of the elderly, digestive symptoms must be examined regularly, to avoid panic and possible emergencies.

## ❧ 27 ❧

# Symptoms of Urinary Diseases

Diseases of the kidneys, bladder, and prostate gland are fairly common in the elderly.

Advancing age, with its attendant decrease in circulation of blood through the kidneys, can cause *uremia*. This condition can lead to death, but usually it can be corrected since it is more apt to occur when the patient's body is depleted of water, as occurs after a spell of vomiting or during a fever. Sometimes the patient simply becomes weak but may be confused or extremely nervous.

Uremia occasionally is brought on by the use of certain drugs or by severe infections of the kidneys and requires medical management.

*Kidney infections* will often cause pain in the small of the back and nearly always there will be irritation of the bladder, causing burning, frequent urination, and scanty urine. The physician can usually, but not always, treat kidney infections and achieve prompt recovery. He will probably test the urine to follow the progress of the disease.

Bladder infections can occur in older women who have a *cystocele*, which is a falling and protrusion of the bladder through the opening of the vagina. Occasionally the uterus will also fall to the outside; this is called a *prolapse of the uterus*. This fallen condition of bladder and womb can be extremely uncomfortable and predispose to bladder infection. If the patient's condition allows, surgery will usually correct the troublesome symptoms.

*Prostate gland* trouble occurs in many elderly men. It is due to enlargement of a gland that surrounds the *urethra*, through which urine passes. When the gland enlarges, it partly blocks the urethra and pushes up on the floor of the bladder. This causes difficulty in urination, hesitancy, straining, dribbling, and occasionally complete blockage of urine.

Symptoms of prostate trouble should be treated promptly before an emergency arises. Surgery may be required. It is remarkable how well elderly patients recover from prostate surgery.

*Kidney stones* become evident with extreme pain over one side of the small of the back, the pain radiating around and down toward the genitals. The urine may become bloody. Often stones will pass without operative intervention, but they do require special care.

Bloody urine from any cause should be investigated by the physician.

# ❧ 28 ❧

# Diseases Affecting the Joints

There are numerous kinds of *rheumatism*, which is a general term for aching in any part of the skeletal structure, muscles, or joints.

The two most common types of *arthritis* are *hypertrophic* and *rheumatoid*. Hypertrophic arthritis may cause stiffness in back, hips, knees, and hands, but seldom is disabling although it may be extremely uncomfortable at times.

An old person may reach advanced age with splayed hands and inability to walk because of rheumatoid arthritis, which usually starts in early adulthood. Occasionally *gout* will cause severe pain in certain joints. This is a poorly understood condition that may cause *tophi* (singular: *tophus*), mineral concretions, in various parts of the body, especially around the joints and at times on the ear.

Joint aches and stiffness are among the most persistent symptoms that the elderly complain of. Their treatment is often exploited by quacks who may charge exorbitant prices for worthless nostrums.

Do not belittle Uncle Albert's weather forecasting by the increased "misery" in his joints. Reduced atmospheric pressure has been proved to increase stiffness in arthritic joints.

While the use of aspirin or one of its variants, the application of heat, the avoidance of fatigue, and reasonable exercise will not overcome arthritis, these remedies and precautions will prevent arthritis from overcoming the patient.

In severe cases, the physician will consider various tests and more elaborate treatment but generally such treatment should be avoided if possible because of its potential dangers.

# 29

# Skin Symptoms

Although the *skin* is easily accessible to examination, it is often neglected until serious disease presents itself. Any persistent sore on the skin, especially on the face, should be examined by a physician. *Skin cancer* is curable if treated promptly, yet people may wait until a large, ulcerating cancer develops before seeking help.

Many people get scaly, wartlike growths on the surface of the abdomen and chest. These sometimes run in families; no treatment is required.

Any brownish moles that change in size should probably be removed.

A person may get *hives*, a fleeting, itching condition with many red patches which come and go. This distressing condition lasts perhaps a day or two and is likely to be associated either with nervousness or certain medicines. If severe it should be treated.

Too little care is given to the circulation in the lower extremities of elderly people. Many are afflicted with *calluses* and *bunions*, and feet that are cold most of the time. Sores or infections of the feet can be a source of trouble in the old, especially the diabetic. Keeping the feet warm is important. Feet should be bathed daily in warm soapy water, dried, and then anointed with vanishing cream. Brushless shaving cream is a good skin conditioner, since it is cheap and not at all messy.

*Foot hygiene* will often prevent serious complications that could result in amputations. Daily foot care ought to be a household motto with regard to elderly folk.

Special care of the skin for the bed patient is discussed in Chapters 41 and 43.

# ❦ 30 ❦

# Systemic Diseases of the Aged

Systemic diseases are those which affect the entire body. In the elderly, the following are the most common: diabetes, hardening of the arteries, *osteoporosis* (thin bones), vitamin deficiencies, thyroid disorders, and anemia. Of these, diabetes is by far the most prevalent. In elderly patients, however, diabetes that develops late in life is usually not a severe malady provided it is recognized. There may be undue dryness of the mouth, frequent urination, change in vision, or loss of weight. The urine or, preferably, the blood, should be checked for sugar about twice a year—more often if diabetes has occurred in other members of the family.

Excessive sugar in the blood can generally be controlled by a tablet prescribed by the doctor, but if injections of insulin are necessary, don't resist; its use may be lifesaving. With diabetes, care of the feet is important because the circulation is more apt to be poorer than among other patients.

The diet for a diabetic should be virtually sugar-free. The appropriate diet for diabetics differs, so that it is well to follow the doctor's advice.

It is important for the elderly diabetic to be in close touch with a physician, eat properly, and take care of his feet.

"Hardening of the arteries"—*arteriosclerosis*—is used by some to explain nearly every symptom from mild giddiness to the numbness in the feet. It may refer to the stiffening ("hardening") of blood-vessel walls which begins in youth and progresses as a normal aging process.

A particular kind of arteriosclerosis is a disease called *atherosclerosis* in which fatty deposits called *plaques* occur irregularly along certain arteries and may predispose to strokes, heart attacks, and other serious maladies. The condition is prone to occur in the elderly, and more severely in diabetics and those with certain other systemic disorders.

Occasionally, when a blood vessel is nearly blocked by a plaque, a person will have abrupt, repeated cramps in the calves of the legs while walking, requiring him to stop for relief. Let your doctor know about such pains at the next visit; they may be serious.

Atherosclerosis may have complications in which surgery would be urgent to relieve an obstructed blood vessel. Such surgery is itself dangerous and often not worth the risk or effort.

Diet treatment has been used to relieve or prevent atherosclerosis. In the elderly, rigid dieting is too late to help the blood vessels. Don't take the joy of eating from an old person by fussy, but misdirected, efforts to "do something." On the other hand, if Grandfather doesn't object and even enjoys talking about his treatment, a low-fat, low cholesterol diet won't hurt him.

A plaque can cause angina pectoris, which I mentioned in Chapter 25.

Thinning of the bones occurs in most old people and accounts for the rounded backs, stooped shoulders, and knobby knees of the elderly. It accounts for much of the rheumatism they endure and the fragility of bones in elderly folk. The cause of bone thinning is not known, but two factors are a deficiency of sex hormones and a low-calcium diet. Occasionally, when severe bone pain occurs, the physician may prescribe a course of *hormone treatment.* Some relief is gained in some cases; at least it can be tried.

In America, which has an abundant supply of food, vitamin deficiencies are seldom seen except in the elderly. Old people who live alone may not eat enough fruits, vegetables, butter, cereals, and milk. One way to assure an aged patient a well-balanced diet is to feed him all kinds of vegetable soups which are rich in vitamins.

Vitamin deficiencies are usually recognized by excessively dry skin, lack of energy, a slick red tongue, cracks at the corners of the mouth, sensitiveness to sunlight, poor night vision, and in other ways. These can be treated with adequate diet and vitamin capsules. However, prevention is easier than treatment.

Occasionally an old person will have a *goiter*—a swelling of the *thyroid gland,* which is in the front area of the neck. This bump may be an active goiter, which will cause sweating, heart racing, and loss of weight. These symptoms can occur with other ailments, but if a goiter is present these symptoms demand a careful examination. In fact, any kind of swelling should be checked by the doctor.

If the thyroid is underactive, the patient may become tired and sleepy; he may feel cold at all times. The voice may become husky. These symptoms suggest *myxedema.* The condition, if present, can be easily treated.

If a vigorous old person becomes excessively tired for no apparent reason, he may be anemic. He may become pale and exhausted. If he has anemia, the cause should be sought. Frequently bleeding from the digestive system or bowel may be the cause. The so-called iron-deficiency anemia we hear so much about is due to a diet deficient in fresh meat and leafy vegetables, or to chronic loss of blood.

In this chapter I have endeavored to stress a few symptoms of systemic disease which are fairly often seen. These symptoms, for the most part, if recognized, can be treated satisfactorily by the alert physician.

Do not discuss symptoms at great length with elderly people. Listen attentively to any unusual complaints—and report to the doctor anything that provokes alarm.

# { 31 }

# How Acute Illness Affects Old People

In preceding chapters a number of acute illnesses have been discussed. Here I want to emphasize the difference between old and young in regard to acute physical problems.

In acute infections, the old person may have less clearly defined symptoms. In pneumonia, for example, his disease may not follow a cold as it usually does in younger people. He may simply become weak and pale and have lung disease distinguishable only by a doctor's examination or by X ray.

Fever is usually less pronounced than in the young, and pain responses are frequently less acute. Appendicitis or even more serious disease may occur with very little pain.

In the elderly, all kinds of complications may develop from a specific illness, and it is these that may give the physician greatest concern. Some of the more prevalent are uremia and heart and lung complications.

During acute illness, there is more likelihood that bladder and bowel symptoms will occur. Prostatism, fecal impaction, and cystocele, which I have discussed earlier, are much more apt to become troublesome.

Generally, if an old person is going about his usual routine, fretting about some ache or pain but eating and drinking normally, his complaint can be handled in a routine way. If, on the other hand, in the course of a day he loses energy and interest and seems to want to stay in bed, medical attention is called for.

# ❦ 32 ❧

# Accidents and Emergencies

Every home should have an emergency plan prepared before the need for it arises. What do you do if, for example, Grandfather faints in the bathroom? Has he been cautioned never to lock himself in? A better plan is to remove bathroom locks when there are old people in the house.

Accident prevention was discussed in Chapter 10 in connection with preparing living quarters for the old person. However, in spite of all precautions, accidents can occur. One of the most common with the aged is a fall which results in a fracture of the hip bone. This can be serious because it may be the first link in a chain of events that lead to death from infection, heart problems, uremia, and so on. When an elderly person suffers a fall, don't force him to his feet at once. Leave him alone, put a pillow under his head and, if necessary, a blanket over him, and call an ambulance. He should be carried to a hospital for emergency examination. Do not move an old person any more than necessary after an accident, but if he can move himself the chance of serious injury is slight.

Other emergencies requiring medical care have already

been mentioned: coronary thrombosis; pulmonary edema; severe abdominal colic; severe bleeding from the digestive system, and persistent kidney colic.

If any of these emergencies arise, call the doctor and follow his orders. If you cannot readily locate your doctor, call an ambulance and have the patient taken to the hospital to which his doctor is affiliated.

In nearly any emergency where the patient is short of breath, give him fresh air, prop him up, or allow him to sit in a chair. His clothing should be loosened.

All doctors are aware of the possibility of sudden death, and everyone knows of instances, either within personal acquaintance or among public figures. A noted statesman, Alben Barkley, died suddenly at the conclusion of a speech, after having made a thousand similar speeches previously. Adlai Stevenson, American Ambassador to the U.N., fell dead on a London street.

An elderly woman called me because of a mild "choking" in her chest; on lying down to be examined, she lapsed into unconsciousness and could not be revived. Another elderly patient dropped dead a day or two after being thoroughly examined. Still another died suddenly in the hospital several days after seemingly successful major surgery.

In nearly every instance these were relatively healthy persons. Relatives wonder about the doctor's competence when sudden death takes one of their own. If the doctor has checked blood pressure, listened for signs of irregular heartbeat, and has taken an electrocardiogram, he has done his duty.

Sudden death is nearly always due to a type of heart condition known as *cardiac arrest* or *cardiac standstill*. The heart simply stops beating.

Rapping sharply on the front of the chest over the left side has been known to restore the normal heartbeat. It is worth a try.

It is, I believe, a misconception to think of strokes as a cause of sudden death. Strokes take minutes to months to kill a victim. If a stroke is suspected, the patient should be turned on his side so that he will not strangle on his saliva or on his tongue, which should be drawn out and held with a handkerchief between the thumb and forefinger until some better means is found. See Chapter 33 for a discussion of strokes and their treatment.

Bleeding seldom causes sudden death, although death may ensue quickly after massive bleeding has been recognized. I was once called to see a very old woman patient; after a brief discussion with her daughter I learned that the patient had been pale and had passed a large black bowel movement. When I went upstairs I found her dead.

*Suffocation* can kill suddenly. A large number of people have choked on food particles or vomitus. If a person should appear to be choking, put his head and chest face down, off the edge of a bed or a pile of cushions and rap sharply between his shoulder blades. It may be too late but it is worth a try.

# ❧ 33 ❧

# Strokes

When a person has a *stroke*, there is a temporary or permanent obstruction to the flow of blood to the brain. This obstruction causes part of the brain to lose its function.

What are the symptoms? They can vary from a temporary lapse of memory to complete paralysis of all the limbs. Sometimes a stroke will cause paralysis of one side of the face, which is seen as a sagging at one side of the mouth. Occasionally it will be shown by extreme *vertigo*, a condition in which the room seems to spin and which is followed by a state of confusion.

Sometimes only one limb will become weak, but the most common result of stroke is *hemiplegia*, in which one entire side of the body is paralyzed. If the flow of blood to the speech center is blocked, a person may lose the ability to speak clearly. This condition is known as *aphasia*. Hemiplegia can be serious and even fatal, but most often the person will survive but be left crippled. He may lack strength and may suffer a loss of mobility in his arm and leg. He will probably have a *foot drop*, so that he cannot lift his toes from the floor.

Many stroke patients undergo a change in personality, becoming highly emotional, crying or laughing without apparent cause. Some will become childish and petulant.

Amazingly, however, stroke patients may recover so well that the stroke cannot even be detected. In dealing with strokes, bear in mind that you are dealing not only with a very sick patient whose brain is not functioning well, but also with a deeply troubled person who may be despondent because his perceptions are weak and he cannot think straight, walk without faltering, or control his toilet functions.

What is the best management of a stroke patient? Many believe that any stroke patient should be hospitalized at once. On the other hand, a number of stroke patients do well at home. The hospital has little to offer but bed care, and to put an old person in unfamiliar surroundings to endure the typical routine of bells, parades of personnel, and commotion can actually be harmful. With strokes, as in other illnesses, old people are often pushed around and shunted hither and yon not for their own benefit but to calm the needless anxiety of relatives.

The doctor's advice is usually sound. He knows how he can best take care of the stroke patient. He will decide what medicines might do some good. He can order the necessary nursing procedures. But do not ask him to make an accurate prognosis. In the early stages of a stroke it is impossible to predict the course of the affliction.

A debility that occasionally follows strokes is Parkinsonism, or Parkinson's disease, named for the early nineteenth-century physician James Parkinson. This condition may come on gradually in the absence of a stroke. At its worst it may be marked by tremors of hands and feet, drooling, an impassive expression of the face, and a tendency to fall forward. The whole body may be somewhat rigid. The symptoms may be severe or mild; at times only one symptom may be present. The disease is not necessarily progressive. Many patients have only a mild tremor which is not disabling. No doubt everyone has observed elderly people with this ailment, which is due to degeneration in a particular area of the brain. In severe cases medicines can be of great help. In rare instances brain surgery would be in order.

Following a stroke, most patients become nursing problems, since they are weak, crippled, unable to control their natural functions, or have a combination of these conditions.

# ❧ 34 ❧

# Mental Illness

It has been estimated that nearly half the patients entering mental hospitals for the first time are over sixty years of age. I am concerned here with forms of behavior which could be dangerous to the patient or to others. Such an illness is called a *psychosis* when the person becomes irrational and is not responsible for his actions.

The dividing line between simple nervousness or peculiarity and psychotic behavior is difficult to determine. Great injustice has been done in calling a perfectly sane person crazy; tragedies have resulted from failing to see that a psychotic person was not responsible for his behavior.

Doctors who treat large numbers of elderly people are frequently caught in emotion-charged situations where they recognize a psychosis that a relative cannot accept. I recall an elderly woman who, despite all attempts to alleviate her suffering, continued to scream with pain, although she showed no physical disease. It was obvious that she was suffering from *hysteria* and needed the care of a psychiatrist. After many months of anguish, her daughters agreed to put her in a mental hospital where, with suitable treatment, she made an eventual recovery.

Occasionally a person will become so despondent that he would rather not live, and indeed is in danger of committing suicide. Much has been written about depressions and suicide; here I merely want to mention some symptoms that show when depression may be dangerous. Usually the person will recite a monotonous story of sadness and doom which may or may not have some basis of truth. He will repeat his concern over and over, endlessly. A depressed patient of mine had a benign prostate condition. Convinced that it was cancer in spite of all evidence to the contrary, he slashed his throat with a razor on the eve of an operation that would have cured him.

An elderly, comfortably well-off widow developed an obsession about money. She thought that she could not afford to pay her grocery bills. She stopped eating. After losing forty pounds in six months, during which a number of wasting diseases had been considered as causing the loss of weight, she was taken to an institution, where care and psychiatric treatment brought about recovery.

There are other obsessions besides those of cancer and financial disaster, among them the obsessive notions that a strange germ is eating away at one's vitals, that a prowler is lurking around the house with harmful intent, that the food has been poisoned, that the world is coming to an end, and so on. An obsession becomes dangerous when it interferes with a person's efficiency and rest and when it becomes a pressing concern of others. In such cases the attending physician may recommend a psychiatrist.

More dangerous are the *paranoid delusions* in which a person "knows" in his heart, though he lacks reasonable evidence, that someone is trying to mistreat him—usually a relative or neighbor. Occasionally, a very old man takes a notion that his faithful elderly wife has been untrue to him. This has occasionally led to tragedy when the demented man seeks revenge with gun, knife, or poison. Behind such behavior there is often a background of jealousy, spite, and feelings of inferiority. Institutional care becomes a necessity.

Far more frequent mental disorders are those caused by memory defects and consequent faulty orientation. Normal memory failures in aging people should not cause undue anxiety. But there are those who lose track of time, place, and identity, and such individuals may be suffering from *senile dementia*. They must be put in an institution. Certainly a person who cannot remember to turn off the gas, to blow out a match, to go to the bathroom, or to walk safely down a flight of stairs cannot be left alone. I recall a tragic result when an elderly woman was unable to remember that a certain door did not lead to the closet but opened on the basement stairs. Obviously the door should have been locked, when it was evident that her memory was failing. Instead of taking practical action, troubled relatives lecture and threaten poor demented old people, which is not only useless but causes additional anxiety in the helpless individual.

A fairly frequent mental disturbance is *delirium*, which occurs in acute illness or drug intoxication. The person will not know where he is or what day of the week it is; he may seem frightened and have horrible visions of strange creatures crawling over the bed. This sort of delirium, except when associated with chronic alcoholism, usually clears up promptly when the general condition improves.

*Delirium tremens* presents a similar picture but occurs in chronic alcoholics. I have seen it in old people I had not previously suspected of being alcoholic.

Occasionally a change of surroundings may induce a

delirious state, as when a patient is taken to a hospital. The patient may be disturbed by shadows which seem to menace him. Poor orientation and restlessness may follow an operation and are not necessarily serious symptoms.

These are not the only symptoms that indicate irresponsible behavior, but they give some idea of what may be expected.

In rare cases, an individual will show a combination of mental aberrations such as forgetfulness and hostility. Such a person will forget who the supposed enemy is, and lash out with a cane, or throw objects, or soil himself seemingly on purpose.

*Tranquilizers* have been the subject of much discussion in recent years. There are many kinds with varying effects. Relatives of patients expect too much from them, but frequently a pill can make an extremely anxious, hostile, sleepless, disagreeable patient fairly comfortable and much easier to nurse. Experimentation may be needed to determine the best drug and dosage. Do not be discouraged or alarmed by unpleasant effects such as giddiness, drowsiness, dryness of the mouth, irregularity of natural functions, and nervous tremors. But do not make the mistake, either, of blaming all symptoms on the medicine. Skip two or three doses, and the physician will be able to decide which symptoms were caused by the drug.

Demented behavior obviously requires constant watchfulness and sometimes institutional care. Treatment depends in large measure upon the physical vitality of the patient. A paranoid man with the strength to walk or wield a club requires different treatment from the feeble old lady who leads a chair-and-bed existence and can't recognize the sensation of a full bladder. The former may have to be put in a mental institution; the latter may be satisfactorily nursed at home.

What kind of institution— a general hospital, a nursing home, a psychiatric hospital? Let the doctor decide.

For acute delirium with fever which cannot be managed at home, a general hospital is recommended. A fairly docile patient who merely needs close nursing supervision needs only nursing-home care. A deeply disturbed, combative patient who requires physical restraint should have psychiatric supervision in a specialized hospital.

The arrangements made depend partly on financial resources, of course. All states maintain mental hospitals which treat patients at little or no cost to the family. At the other extreme are very luxurious psychiatric institutions which are similar in their appointments to resort hotels. The care given in the state mental hospital is often as good as and sometimes better than that given at Shady Grove Sanatorium; on the other hand, the care at Shady Grove may be as much superior as the accommodations. In every case the individual institution must be investigated.

Families also often expect too much in the way of improvement. When Grandfather doesn't improve at Shady Grove, and the family is near bankruptcy, calm judgment dictates moving him to State Mental. Actually, he would probably have been less disturbed, anguish could have been prevented, and great sums saved, if he had not gone first to Shady Grove.

If he is willing to go to Shady Grove and resists going to State Mental, he can be treated until arrangements are made to have him committed, which involves legal procedure.

Commitment procedure varies from state to state. It is usually necessary under two circumstances: (1) if a person is unwilling to receive the care required for public and personal safety; (2) if the relatives cannot or will not assume financial responsibility.

It is heartbreaking when it is necessary to go to court to have an elderly person carried bodily to a mental hospital. In spite of the anguish, if the person is dangerous to himself or to others, do not hesitate. Many times I have recommended commitment early in the week, the relatives have been reluctant, and then the patient has become violent on the weekend when legal machinery was unavailable.

In many instances psychiatric treatment can be helpful to the aged. Constant nursing care, tranquilizers, a change in routine, or an altered home situation will help the patient and brighten the perspective of those responsible for him.

# ❦ 35 ❧

# Considering a Nursing Home

Sooner or later, the problems of caring for an aged invalid in your home may become so serious that you will have to decide whether you should put him in a nursing home. This, like the move to the family home, is a serious decision requiring much thought. When you are debating such a step, the answers to the following questions should help you reach your decision.

Is the person too heavy, too disabled, too depressed, to be adequately nursed at home? (In this connection, home means the family home, as distinguished from a nursing home.)

Is the home too crowded to have an out-and-out invalid occupying space needed for family living?

Are the people at home capable of nursing? Can outside help be obtained? Can the patient be left alone at times?

Is medical attention more readily available at home or in the nursing home?

113

Which is more feasible economically, extra help at home or the expense of a nursing home?

How does an invalid affect others in the home, especially children?

Will the invalid be happier at home or where he can be given constant nursing care?

If you have decided to consider a nursing home for your aged relative, what do you look for? Here you need answers to another set of questions.

What standards does the prospective nursing home have? Is it approved for Medicare benefits?

What will it cost? What does the price include? How much of the cost will be paid by insurance and how much will have to be met by the patient or his family?

Is the nursing home approved by and does it co-operate with any insurance plans to which your relative may be entitled? Will public welfare funds pay any part of the cost?

Do the people on the staff appear to be competent? Can you conscientiously trust your relative to them?

Are they interested, kind, and concerned? Have you observed their activities at various times of the day? Is the evening shift as able as the morning contingent? Are there enough people to get the job done?

Are the accommodations suitable and cheerful? Is adequate regard given to light, safety, cleanliness, toilet facilities, and recreation?

Do most of the patients seem to be reasonably contented and cheerful?

Is the food well prepared and appetizing (allowing for special diets, of course)?

Nursing homes today often have long waiting lists. Try to plan ahead. Find out when the nursing home of your choice will be able to take your relative.

In reaching a decision about the nursing home, the feelings of the patient should be considered. In many cases, the individual himself has reached the conclusion that it would be better for him to leave home. His family has shown him every evidence of kindness; however, what he fears most is that he has become a burden.

Before asking an old person to decide about a nursing home, the family should hold a conference. It is my experience that too often an aged father or mother is made the sole responsibility of one son or daughter. This responsibility may be taken because a particular member of the family is more loving or kind than the others, perhaps because the parents were partial to this one in earlier times. Whatever the reason, it is an ugly spectacle when children try to even up old resentments over the wasted, prostrate body of an aged invalid.

Now is the time for cooperation. Can John assume responsibility for so much a month? Can Cora pay so much? Maybe one cannot afford as much as another; in that case the sum should be figured proportionally.

Such arrangements are so much happier than the pettiness and spite that too often sadden the doctor.

In reaching a decision, do not say to Grandfather: "Dad, how would you like to go to a nursing home?"

Instead, say, "We have made arrangements for you to go to Elmwood for a while until you are better. We'll see you every day." This is positive and does not remove all hope of improvement or return.

Do not discuss the move with Dad until shortly before; its anticipation is dreadful to him. Don't keep him mystified and bewildered by putting him in what seems a strange and hostile place. In general, the preparations for moving will be similar to those suggested in Chapter 9.

Grandfather is finally ensconced at Elmwood and is bewildered by the strange routine and by other patients who may feel as bad as he. Is he going to like it? Of course not. The point I'm making is that old people detest change. Don't panic because he doesn't like it at first. The doctor can prescribe a tranquilizer for a few days until the patient becomes used to the people and the routine.

After a week or two, with frequent visits, Grandfather will probably feel that he is better off than he had been in months.

What of the family—John, Cora, and the rest? They are paying good money at Elmwood so that Dad can be well cared for by competent aides. Shouldn't he be getting better?

A nursing home, no matter how expensive, cannot assure health or contentment. Remember that Dad would not be there if he could be expected to get much better.

Nursing homes do not provide private nurses who can devote all their attention to one patient.

Does a nursing home give assurance that Grandmother won't fall and suffer a hip fracture? No, it doesn't. It should provide hand rails, smooth floors, and strollers to help with walking, but it can't give assurance that a patient will not fall and sustain an injury.

Nor can it guarantee that a patient will not soil himself two minutes before his visitors arrive.

Do not judge the nursing home by the care Grandfather gets in the first two weeks. After that, if he is continually soiled, is losing weight, feeling worse, unkempt, and despondent, then—but only then—serious consideration may be given to transferring him elsewhere.

During the first few days in a nursing home he ought to

have visitors morning, noon, and afternoon. Children and grandchildren should visit almost at all hours during daylight—not all together, but preferably one or two at a time. Do not allow Grandfather to dwell too long on his symptoms, and by all means encourage an optimistic view of his surroundings, unpleasant though they may seem to him at first.

# ❧ 36 ❧

# Homes for Active Old People

Other than nursing homes, homes for the aged are a fairly recent institution. Unfortunately, the distinction between the two is not understood as well as it should be. Indeed, many of these places make no real distinction. Fortunately, rapid progress is being made in housing and accommodations for the healthy elderly.

Where it is unsuitable for Grandfather to live with a son or daughter, it is best to consider all the possibilities. To put a fairly spry man of seventy in a nursing home hardly seems appropriate. The presence of pale, suffering, wasted, disoriented elderly people who need constant nursing care would be exceedingly depressing.

Why should he move at all? Reread Chapter 7, "When to Start Living Together," which could almost be read to mean "reasons for moving." The snow in winter, the grass in summer, the isolation, the uncertainty, the inability to cook and clean, are all good and sufficient reasons for Grandfather to move.

Why shouldn't he live with one of his children? The

answer may be that he likes his independence and his only son and his family live a thousand miles away. Grandfather doesn't want to leave his friends of a lifetime; he would miss the lodge meetings and the Civic Committee activities. He would be lost being anonymous in a strange locality where no one knows him or what he has done for his community.

Grandfather might be able to rent an apartment in a private dwelling and make arrangements for his meals, as so many people do.

Many downtown apartments in large cities now specialize in meeting the needs of alert aged tenants.

Church denominations are now, with government help, in the business of supplying homes for the aged.

Friendship Manor in Roanoke, Virginia, with which I am most familiar, is not a nursing home but actually a "complete care center" for the aged. Since homes of its type are of fairly recent development, and since I believe they will become more prevalent in the future, I'll describe it in some detail.

It is on a large tract of land at the edge of the city. The yard, flowers, and garden are beautiful and offer a physical outlet for the energies of a number of the men who live there. Some of the women enjoy tending the flowers that border the walks. Apartments are available for elderly married couples who prefer to do their own cooking. Those who don't wish to prepare their own food may take their meals in a central dining room.

It is light, modern, and cheerful. The buildings are constructed for the purpose they serve, and thus accident prevention enters into the plan. The home was built according to the ideas expressed in Chapter 10, "Arranging Living Quarters."

Activities abound but no one is forced to take part in any. Mealtime in the dining room is a social occasion three times a day. There is good public transportation for those able to use it. Anyone who is able to drive a car may do so. There are frequent group excursions to shopping centers and cultural and religious occasions.

There are parlors with kitchen nooks for entertaining clubs and organizations. The dining room welcomes guests at modest cost. There is a chapel, beauty shop, and self-service laundry. Maid service is available at extra cost to those unable to tidy their own rooms.

One floor, removed from the main part of the building, serves as the infirmary for the ill or for those who have become so feeble as to require nursing care. The nurse in the infirmary can be summoned to any room in the building by pulling an alarm switch. The helpless and dying residents cannot cast a pall over the premises because they are not seen unless by intention.

For the most part, the people are of similar cultural, religious, and economic backgrounds. These similarities are conducive to harmony, understanding, and good cheer.

People may bring in their own furniture to equip their quarters. Private telephones can be installed; some people spend hours talking with friends or planning activities.

The more vigorous help those less capable with compassion and good fellowship.

The costs are low because it is operated by a non-profit, tax-exempt organization. Roughly these are $200 a month for a large single room and bath with board to $375 for nursing-care accommodations.

It is hoped that such facilities will become more numerous because they seem to be a real answer to a pressing problem.

Some resort areas have retirement villages and apartments at varying financial arrangements. Generally, though, an elderly person will be happier if he can be close to the familiar surroundings of a lifetime.

# ❧ 37 ❧

# Can a Hospital Help?

Elsewhere I have spoken of the problems involved in taking an elderly person to the hospital. This chapter is concerned with what can be expected of treatment there.

Remember when a hospital was exclusively for surgery or serious illness? The stay was apt to be prolonged, and nursing service was thorough, personal, and dedicated. Those were the "good old days" when complete rest, even unto death, was considered to be the best treatment. Then, hospitals had little to offer but rest and nursing. A good many of us can recall the old order of things and expect a modern hospital to give the old-time service. Alas, a rude awakening is in store for those who cling to such notions when they bring an elderly member of the family for a rest cure or a minor illness.

Hospitals have become larger, more complex, far more expensive, and geared to rendering service to a far greater number of patients. Consequently many hospitals, even among the best, are overcrowded and understaffed.

Daughters complain to me when no one comes around

to feed a helpless parent while they sit idly visiting. I promptly suggest they feed him themselves. Why not?

Except when expensive private nursing is available, relatives will usually have to sit with the patient most of the time he is awake. They can help feed him and generally be on hand to call for help. Most hospitals simply do not have enough personnel to give individual care to helpless patients. Never mind, of course, if the patient is spry and partly able to look after his own needs, can get to the bathroom without assistance, and can handle the electric gear, present in most hospitals, to call for help when necessary.

More often than not, the facilities for which various insurance plans will pay are not available at any price. Some plans will pay for a private nurse, but the plan cannot guarantee that you'll get one at any time you call. Some plans will pay for a private room that is nonexistent. Some plans will pay for two doctor visits a day, and the doctor in charge may make only one.

We feel mistreated if what we can pay for is unavailable and tend to blame the doctor, the hospital, or both. This is most unfair, makes for hard feelings, and, worst of all, is upsetting to the patient.

Too often doctors, at the insistence of the family, put an aged parent in the hospital "for a checkup," only to aggravate the distress and discomfort of the patient.

Sometimes a hospital, instead of helping, can do a lot of harm. For example, Uncle Frank is fairly comfortable getting about at home, from bed to toilet to table to chair. Then his appetite lessens and he loses a little weight. His family worries and his doctor puts the old gentleman into the hospital.

He is not used to the food, the routine, the nurses. Like anyone else he becomes confused; he doesn't drink enough water; he tries to get out of bed, falls, breaks a hip, and eventually dies. This sequence of events occurs with much more regularity than people realize. The point I make is that hospitals can be risky places, particularly for the old.

Hospitals impose visiting regulations; these are enforced. Where a visitor's presence is necessary to the patient's safety, hospitals will often relax their stringency.

Hospital food is as good (and as tasteless) as most institutional food but is often tepid when it arrives, because it has to be transported from a distant kitchen. A visitor might be helpful by serving the food when it first arrives.

If the patient is assigned to a ward in an emergency, a different accommodation can be requested of the hall nurse. Don't bother the doctor about it; he has no jurisdiction

The length of stay in the hospital can become a matter of dissension. The physician may say Mother can go home, but daughter, who has been having it a little easier during her mother's absence, may want her to remain, because the insurance will cover it. Let the doctor decide. He not only has Mother and daughter to consider, but other patients, an insurance company or two, and a hospital committee. Increasingly, the doctor has an obligation to get people out of the hospital as quickly as he safely can. This usually works to the advantage of the patient because of the hospital-risk factor, and because some old people become "spoiled" into not doing for themselves what they might do.

Hospitals set a time for signing in and out for non-emergency treatment. This is done so that costs can be accurately computed, and as a matter of orderliness.

The doctor won't be a good source of information about hospital rates, except in a general way. All hospitals nowadays have specially trained people who can advise about

Medicare, Medicaid, various hospital group plans, and private hospital insurance. On admission or soon after, take any insurance policies and confer with the clerk in the business office of the hospital.

Much anxiety is caused when laboratory tests and X rays are needed. If a doctor says he wants to get a *G.I. series*, he means he wants to get a series of X rays of the digestive, or gastrointestinal system. A *barium enema* is an enema with a barium solution which reveals the outline of the bowel on the X-ray film. A *gall-bladder series* is similar to a G.I. series, except that it outlines the gall bladder and bile tubes. An IVP (*introvenous pyelogram*) is a series of X rays, after injecting a dye solution into a vein, to outline the urine-collecting system of the kidneys. *Arteriograms* are most often made in various types of brain disease and are X-ray outlines of arteries which have been injected with a dye solution.

There are many more kinds of X-ray procedures, but those mentioned are among the more common. Don't always expect a full explanation of every procedure; the doctor knows what he is doing and will explain whatever is necessary.

X rays take time and study. However anxious you may be, don't call a doctor's office for a hospital X-ray report. He probably hasn't received it, and it is a waste of time.

Frequent laboratory tests are:

*Blood count*—a determination of the number of cells of various kinds in the blood giving an indication of disease.

*Urinalysis*—a urine test—may indicate various systemic disorders such as diabetes, as well as kidney and bladder disease.

There are hundreds of blood-chemistry tests suggesting all kinds of disorders. There is no reason to ask for lengthy explanations of what they possibly could mean.

Of great importance in putting an elderly person in the hospital is that it be done with a happy, positive approach. Do not complain unduly about food or service. Such assurances as "We're going to stay with you," "They're going to take good care of you," "Isn't Miss Jones a nice nurse?" go much further than negative remarks such as, "It looks like Dr. Brown will never get here!" or "I never saw such a place!" or "The food isn't fit for human consumption!" The approach is the same with Grandmother going to the hospital as going to school with a fearful child on the first day: be cheerful, calm, and positive.

The doctor makes his rounds in the hospital about the same time each day. Some one member of the family could be delegated to get a report at such a time.

Have no fear if there is a serious complication. The physician will undoubtedly be trying to get in touch with some member of the family.

Do not encourage a parade of visitors to the bedside. The hospital routine is strenuous enough for the patient without his having to endure a constant chorus of greetings and admonitions. I have often groaned at seeing a patient's six children, several children-in-law, and even more grandchildren hovering about. Never should more than one or two visitors be present at one time, and then only to sit quietly to let the invalid know that the others were thinking of him and wishing the best for him.

Small arrangements of flowers add cheer to a sickroom, but when flowers pile up in a room someone should have the courage to get rid of the oversupply. Banks of flowers may cause allergies; besides, they remind the old of funerals.

Do not hover over a sick person like a mother bird over a nest of young. Excessive washing, combing, straightening, feeding, and fluffing may do wonders for a guilty conscience, but are awfully hard on a feeble old woman.

It is well to be forewarned about what to expect of a hospital and to realize that things may not go well. Yet in many cases the experience will be marked by pleasant memories of devoted people who do a fine job of relieving suffering and prolonging life.

# ❦ 38 ❦

# Elderly People and Surgery

In certain circumstances, of course, a hospital stay is necessary. The most frequent reason is the need for surgery.

In recent years advances in surgery and anesthesia make formerly dangerous operations reasonably safe.

The following conditions for surgery should be considered only as a very general outline. The decisions are made by the attending physician and the surgeon.

Numerous skin conditions may call for surgery Among these are skin cysts, tumors, moles, and horny growths which are familial. Cysts are due to accumulations of skin oils in a cavity varying in size from a pea to a nut; they are called *wens* or *sebaceous cysts*. Unless they become very sore or are unsightly, they can be left alone. Let the doctor decide.

Many people may have a movable, soft, nontender growth beneath the skin called a *lipoma* or *fatty tumor*. These also tend to run in families and can be left alone.

As one grows older, he may develop raised, scaly growths on chest and abdomen, known as *keratosis senilis*. The growths run together and tend to scale or to come off easily. They are often numerous and appear with such freqency that surgery seems useless.

Cataracts may in time require removal, as I have explained earlier.

*Hernias,* which occur particularly in men, often require surgery. They are manifested by swellings in the groin, extending toward the genitals. They can become as large as a grapefruit and may be quite painful. Occasionally they can become serious by causing obstruction of the bladder or bowel. Hernias usually can be repaired safely, although in rare instances they return even after the best surgical treatment.

In women, fallen womb or bladder, called *prolapse of the uterus* or *cystocele,* mentioned earlier, can be annoying and cause bladder infection. Most often it can be satisfactorily treated surgically.

*Hemorrhoids*—swollen veins at the opening of the rectum—should be operated on only if they are exceedingly painful or bleed often. Hemorrhoids should always be examined for possibly more serious conditions.

Painful, swollen veins in the legs are called *varicose veins* and may lead to discoloration of the lower limbs or to big oozing sores called *varicose ulcers.* These may require repeated surgical treatment; they seldom cause prolonged disability.

*Prostatism,* or *enlargement of the prostate gland,* common in elderly men, often calls for surgical treatment. This is usually not malignant but may result from cancer. However, cancer of the prostate can often be treated successfully.

# ❧ 39 ❧

# Rehabilitating the Aged Patient

Rehabilitation of the patient means restoring him as nearly as possible to the condition he was in before the onset of illness. The process of aging does not allow for complete rehabilitation, but many diseases and injuries do respond to various procedures.

In cases of stroke (see Chapter 33) many things can be of great help in restoring maximum function. More than anything else, a stroke victim needs moral support, the assurance that he is wanted and loved. This perhaps is the keystone of all rehabilitation procedures. Too often doctors get loud complaints within the hearing of patients about what a nuisance they are. To complain in the presence of a disabled old person is inhuman.

After an acute illness most physicians prefer to have a patient sitting in a chair at the earliest practicable moment. This should not occasion alarm, because the physician knows that congestion of the lungs, pneumonia, blood clots in the lungs—and in the legs (*phlebitis*)—are much more apt to occur when patients lie in bed for prolonged periods. Such complications killed many old people before surgery for broken hips enabled the patient to leave the bed sooner.

A stroke patient who is paralyzed on one side of the body can often be propped in a chair within a few days. This is of great help to his morale.

As the stroke patient regains some function in face or extremities he can be given a course of exercises to help him in the proper use of muscles that are beginning to respond. He can be told: "Raise your arm. Lift your foot." Be sure the demands are reasonable. Being told to do something impossible only disheartens the patient. Generous praise should be given for each small accomplishment.

Later, the stroke patient may be able to stand if given support. Then walking with help, walking between bars or with a stroller, and finally walking without help can sometimes be accomplished.

If a foot drop occurs, a foot brace may be of help. Such braces may also be a hindrance; only a trial can prove their efficacy.

The joints of a paralyzed limb tend to become stiff. This should be counteracted by making sure that the joints get exercise or are gently bent within the normal range of motion, either by a nurse or relative. Sometimes this bending is a little painful but it should be tried three or four times a day within the limit of the patient's willingness. Such bending tends to prevent *contractures*, whereby joints become bent and fixed in a position that does not permit normal use.

The knees most often tend to contract and for this reason a person should be reminded not to lie with the knees bent. Pillows should be put under the knees only occasionally. Sometimes weights should be attached to the feet to keep the knees straight. The physician will advise what measures are best.

Sometimes stroke patients may have other conditions, such as heart trouble, which prevent active exercise.

Following a heart attack patients are often able to sit in a chair after a week, or do a little slow walking in two or three weeks. The old idea that prolonged absolute rest is an advantage should be discarded. On the other hand, especially with a heart condition in which the patient is short of breath, he cannot be expected to do much walking, if any.

After a siege of pneumonia or an injury, a person should be encouraged to be up as soon as can be managed. However, do not expect him to recover as quickly as a young person would.

In the aged a bruise or fall which seems trivial may still require weeks for recovery. The time needed to get over an infection such as bronchitis will probably be much longer than for the young.

To sum up, the purpose of rehabilitation is to restore function to the maximum degree. This is accomplished by a positive, helpful attitude, the exercise of all usable body functions, and patience and encouragement in the event of failures.

# ❧ 40 ❧

# Diets and Feeding Procedures

Many elderly people have odd notions of what they can and cannot eat. Although the diet habits of some do not make good sense scientifically, it is futile to argue, and mealtime is not the occasion to raise the issue.

Generally, food should be softer and blander than younger people would prefer. Raw fruits and vegetables may cause bloating or cramps, and are best avoided.

An effort should be made to see that the *diet* is balanced and contains enough food value to maintain weight. Ordinarily a normal diet should contain fair quantities of meat, yellow and leafy vegetables, cereals, milk, and some fat, as in butter or cheese.

If a person has a well-balanced diet and eats heartily, supplementary vitamins are not necessary. A finicky eater may need supplementary vitamins, as suggested by the doctor. During illness or following an operation, vitamin deficiencies may become apparent. The patient develops a sore, beef-red tongue, awkwardness in walking, excessively dry skin, and other symptoms. To prevent such complications, the doctor may prescribe vitamins in some form.

Certain advertised products cost a lot more than they are worth; others carry labels that make fraudulent claims. Be sure to read the fine print. Nevertheless, good values can be obtained from established mail-order companies. Consult your doctor about them.

An adequate daily diet should include:

Milk—2 cups or more

Meats, fish, fowl, cheese, and eggs—2 or more servings

Vegetables and fruits—4 or more servings, including dark green or yellow vegetables and citrus fruit or tomatoes

Bread and cereals—or more servings of enriched or whole-grain products

Other foods—fats and sweets to add palatability and variety

### SUGGESTED MEAL PLAN

| *Breakfast* | *Dinner and Supper* | *Bedtime* |
|---|---|---|
| Fruit or juice | Meat or substitute | Fruit juice or |
| Cereal | Potato or substitute | milk |
| Egg | Vegetable or vegetable | |
| Toast, butter, jelly | soup | |
| Milk or cream | Salad—at least once daily | |
| Hot beverage, | Bread and butter | |
| sugar | Dessert or fruit | |
| | Beverage | |

Missing teeth or a finicky digestion may require a soft diet. Select a balanced diet among the following:

Soups: any strained
Meats: strained or ground
Cheese: cottage cheese or cream cheese
Eggs: poached, soft-cooked in shell, soft-scrambled, or eggnog
Potatoes: mashed only
Vegetables: strained vegetables and vegetable juices
Fruits: strained fruits and juices, sliced bananas, frozen strawberries
Cereals: oatmeal, farina, cream of wheat, rice, noodles, macaroni, grits, and spaghetti
Breads: white bread without crust, milk toast (small cubes) with hot milk
Desserts: plain puddings, custards, ice cream, gelatins, and strained fruits
Beverages: as desired, including milk
Fats: butter, margarine, and cream as desired
Others: sugar, jellies; salt and pepper as desired

## SUGGESTED MEAL PLAN

| *Breakfast* | *Dinner and Supper* | *Interval Feedings* |
|---|---|---|
| Fruit | Soup | 10 A.M. Fruit juice |
| Cereal | Meat or substitute | 3 P.M. Milk or |
| Egg | Potato or substitute | coffee |
| Bread without crust | Vegetable | 8 P.M. Coffee or |
| Butter and jelly | Bread without crust | tea, with sugar, |
| Milk | Butter | cream, or milk |
| Hot beverage, sugar and cream or milk if desired | Dessert or fruit | |
| | Beverage | |

If constipation is a problem, prune juice, stewed prunes, or other cooked fruits may be eaten more freely.

In cases of upset digestion a balanced diet selected from the "acceptable foods" in the list on pages 136–138 may be more agreeable; the "foods to avoid" would aggravate the condition.

|  | ACCEPTABLE FOODS | FOODS TO AVOID |
|---|---|---|
| Soups | Cream soup, milk toast | Meat soups, bouillons, and meat gravies |
| Meats | Lean, tender, and well-done beef, veal, lamb, lean fresh pork, poultry, liver, sweetbreads, fish, and oysters. Cook by baking, broiling, stewing or creaming | Smoked and cured meats such as ham, sausage, frankfurters, luncheon meats, corned beef, salt pork; fried meats and rare meats |
| Cheese | Cottage, cream, mild-processed and mild American cheese | Strong-flavored or sharp cheese |
| Eggs | Soft- or hard-cooked, in shell, poached, scrambled | Fried eggs |
| Vegetables | Well-cooked asparagus tips, beets, carrots, string beans, peas, pumpkin, squash, tender leafy greens, white or sweet potatoes; lettuce; cooked or peeled raw tomatoes. Cook vegetables in salted water and season with butter or margarine | Fried and greasy vegetables, gas-forming vegetables such as turnips, onions, cabbage, and dried beans |
| Fruits | Ripe bananas; canned peaches, pears, plums, apricots, sweet cherries, fruit cocktail, apple sauce, peeled baked apple; other peeled fruits if well | Fruit with small seeds, or raw fruit with skin |

|  | tolerated. Orange and grapefruit sections and fruit juices may be used if taken at the end of a meal |  |
|---|---|---|
| Cereals | Cornflakes, corn pop, frosted flakes, puffed rice, rice crisps, oatmeal, cream of wheat, farina, grits, cornmeal, macaroni, spaghetti, noodles, and rice | Whole-wheat and bran cereals; popcorn; pancakes |
| Breads | White bread—plain or toasted, thin baked biscuits and cornbread; soda crackers, saltines, or round crackers | Coarse dark breads and breads with seeds |
| Desserts | Plain desserts such as cakes and cookies with frostings, jello, junket, puddings, fruit and any smooth dessert | Rich desserts such as pies, doughnuts, fruit and nut cakes, cookies |
| Beverages | Milk (sweet milk, buttermilk, or chocolate milk), milkshakes, eggnog, weak cocoa, fruit juices, decaffeinated coffee | Tea, coffee, cola, or alcoholic drinks unless ordered by the physician |
| Fats | Butter, margarine, cream, salad oil, and crisp bacon | Fried and greasy foods |
| Others | Salt, sugars, jelly, honey, cocoa, plain candy, | Highly spiced or seasoned foods; |

|                         | ACCEPTABLE FOODS | FOODS TO AVOID |
|---|---|---|
|  | vanilla, lemon, vinegar, cinnamon, allspice, mace, thyme, sage, and paprika | pepper, chili, cloves, nutmeg, mustard, catsup, pickles, olives |

## SUGGESTED MEAL PLAN

| *Breakfast* | *Dinner and Supper* | *Interval Feedings* |
|---|---|---|
| Fruit | Meat or substitute | 10 A.M. Milk, |
| Cereal, sugar | Potato or substitute | 8 ounces |
| Egg and bacon | Vegetable or soup | 3 P.M. Milk, |
| Toast, butter, jelly | Bread, butter | 8 ounces |
| Milk | Dessert or fruit | 8 P.M. Eggnog, |
| Decaffeinated coffee or weak tea | Milk | 8 ounces |

# { 41 }

# Care of the "Chair-and-Bed" Patient

As a result of old age, accident, or illness, many people are eventually confined to a chair-and-bed existence. Such existence may be permanent, although it is not necessarily so. In any event, it presents certain problems of nursing.

*Clothing* should be comfortable but also practical. High-necked, tight-cuffed "granny" gowns are an abomination to nurse and doctor. They are difficult to keep clean, tend to bunch beneath the patient in bed, and bind her so that she cannot be given proper exercise.

Comfortable gowns that can be opened down the back and which fit loosely are available at surgical supply stores and most department stores. These can be put on while the patient is lying down, and if soiled can be easily removed. They also facilitate the work of doctor and nurse.

Many old people are "cold-natured" and want extra clothing. If so a shawl, wool socks, or a small blanket may be used.

The bed should be firm so that the patient lies comfortably on it without being half-buried in it. A firm bed protects the back from being held in a crooked position which may become painful.

As long as a person can get up by himself he should not have a high hospital bed which requires added effort in climbing in and out. On the other hand, when the patient can no longer get up without assistance a hospital bed can be a great convenience.

Some old-fashioned high beds are still in use, but hospital beds are better because they can be adjusted to different heights. Such beds can be purchased or rented from surgical supply houses, and can also be purchased from mail-order houses and some furniture stores.

Blankets should be as light as possible while still providing sufficient warmth. Heavy, close-knit blankets do not allow for proper air circulation and predispose the patient to skin rashes and poor sanitation. Furthermore they are difficult to launder.

Blankets of light synthetic fibers are now available. These can be washed and dried in an hour or two and are particularly suitable for invalids. Sometimes an electric blanket will prove more practical and comfortable.

Sheets should be wrinkle-free, not starched. Stiffness and wrinkles in sheets predispose to skin irritations.

Bedmaking can be done best if the patient is not in the bed, but the task can be accomplished by rolling the patient to one side, making the bed smooth on the other side, then rolling the patient back onto the smooth side and smoothing the other.

Blankets or bedspread should not be tucked so tight that the feet are stretched or toes are not given room enough to exercise. The feet might be left uncovered, or if this is not comfortable a small box can be put into the bed to allow the toes enough room to wiggle.

When the circulation in the extremities is poor, the physician may prescribe additional warmth. One way of accomplishing this is to get a box large enough for one or both legs, and to put in one or more light bulbs by an extension cord. By using a room thermometer and regulating the number and distance of the bulbs from the bed, any desired temperature can be achieved. Usually where heat for the limbs is desirable it should not be over 105 degrees.

A patient will often be strong enough to sit up but too weak to raise himself from a lying position. He can be helped by placing one hand behind his thighs and another behind his shoulders and swinging his feet off the edge of the bed as he sits. With a little practice this can be easily managed by cooperation of the patient and his helper. If the bed is low, he can then stand on the floor; if it is high, he can step to a stool and then to the floor.

How does one support a very weak patient who is getting out of bed for the first time in weeks or months? Face him as one would in ballroom dancing. Have him put his arms over your shoulders while you put yours around his waist. Retreat as he walks forward, turning as necessary so that at the proper moment the patient can be backed into a chair.

Helping a person to a chair is easier, of course, if the patient can help himself, or if there are two people to help, but the previous method can solve the problem.

What kind of chair should be provided for the patient? Avoid deep overstuffed chairs. Use an armchair with the seat at a comfortable height to rest the feet on the floor. A wheel chair allows a person to remain up most of the day and can be moved from place to place.

If the patient is too weak to go to the bathroom a bedside commode can be made available. The simplest form is an ordinary bedpan placed on a firm, straight chair. Sometimes, studying a mail-order-house catalogue for sickroom supplies is rewarding.

Foot drop has already been mentioned. When a person rests his arms or wrists too long on the arms of a chair, he will sometimes get *wrist drop*, caused by pressure on nerves at the elbows or on the palm side of the forearms. This can be avoided by soft cushioning on the chair arms and by insisting on frequent change of position.

People who spend most of the day sitting in one position may develop puffiness of the legs and ankles— edema. This is frequently of little consequence, being due more to position than to disease, but examination by a physician is usually desirable.

The objectives of nursing are to keep the patient as clean as possible, as comfortable as possible, and as well nourished as possible.

Care can be taken to see that an elderly man is shaved fairly often. This can be done easily with an electric razor.

Turning the patient from side to side allows one to inspect the back for roughness or redness of the skin which may develop into a bed sore and enables one to bathe and powder the patient thoroughly.

Such turning can be achieved by use of a draw sheet, which is simply a folded sheet placed beneath the patient from knees to shoulder. By lifting one side, you can roll the patient one way or the other for bathing or examination. If there is danger of rolling the patient out of bed, a hospital bed with rails may be necessary.

If your patient is recovering from an operation or a stroke and improvement is seen, get him help for walking as soon as he can stand by himself and move his feet. A patient then needs relatively little support. Often he can hold a light, sturdy, straight chair in front of him to give support as he walks. After practicing the patient can be supplied with a stroller, either bought or rented, which offers him support on three sides. The enclosure of a stroller gives the convalescing patient a sense of security. A stroller also enables him to go to the bathroom conveniently and to take his meals with the family.

Hopefully your elderly patient will recover enough to be up and around. If not, more serious nursing problems may arise.

In nursing an old person, one may feel guilty if the patient doesn't get better, especially after the expenditure of enormous effort and considerable money. Inexperienced or unsympathetic relatives can be critical of the nursing given an elderly invalid. The patient in his misery may be spiteful or complaining or unappreciative.

Remember, then, that this is a job that you have undertaken to do properly. Don't let it throw you. Rest and recreation are especially important for the one acting as chief nurse. Share the duties whenever you can.

Feeding a feeble, bedridden patient is not easy. Firmness will get results where a too gentle approach will fail. If an old person has no appetite, any food will do. The problem is getting it down.

Don't ask, "Papa, do you want some beef?" If he has to be fed, he probably doesn't want to eat at all. Say, "Now open your mouth and eat this beef!" The feeder must be bossy in a good-natured way. It saves time. Also, the more an old person is fed the better.

If a person is too weak to eat solid food, or if his teeth are not good enough to chew it, there are a number of ways of feeding. Various prepared soups are tasty, easily digested, economical, well balanced, and convenient. The flavor can be varied from one meal to another.

If the patient cannot swallow solid food, he can be fed a balanced diet in the form of puréed baby food, which can be bought in jars in wide variety. If only liquid can be managed, a number of commercial products provide a complete diet in liquid form.

Spoon feeding can be so tedious that little food is actually swallowed. Occasionally a person can suck through a straw when he cannot take food from a spoon.

If he is unable even to use a straw, food can be put into the mouth with an Asepto Syringe, which is a pointed plastic tube that can be filled by releasing the squeeze on its rubber bulb. Syringes are available at most drugstores. In using one, be sure that the person swallows completely and that the food does not choke him. If the food doesn't go down the right way the patient will cough, even if he is barely conscious.

By using patience and ingenuity a completely adequate diet can sometimes be maintained. On the other hand, if you fail in spite of conscientious effort, do not feel frustrated. The task is filled with difficulties, and all you are capable of is never enough.

More serious nursing problems are described in the next three chapters.

# ❧ 42 ❧

# The Incontinent Patient

The condition in which a patient is unable to control his bladder or bowels is called *incontinence*. It occurs in many very feeble old people who have lost muscular and nerve control. It is frequently associated with disease of bladder, prostate, or bowel. Incontinence may be a temporary condition associated with another illness. It is usually more pronounced in bedridden patients. It can be permanent.

If a man urinates in bed at unpredictable times or has a persistent and constant trickle of urine, disease of the prostate is likely and should be considered by a physician. In the extremely feeble, little can be done; in others, some form of surgery may provide relief.

In a woman, cystocele is often a cause of incontinence; as mentioned earlier, this condition can be relieved by surgery.

If surgery has nothing to offer a person who is constantly wetting the bed, what can be done?

With constant, thorough nursing care the patient may be kept fairly comfortable. An elderly person can be treated in the same way as an infant; keep him fairly dry and comfortable by using diapers and changing them often, drying, bathing, and powdering. Old sheeting, cotton blankets, or toweling can serve as diapers, or they may be purchased. A rubber or plastic sheet can be used beneath a draw sheet.

The danger in allowing a patient to remain wet is that urine is irritating to the skin, especially if it becomes infected with bacteria that form ammonia. In an incontinent patient, the skin is apt to become irritated and to develop bedsores.

If a male patient cannot be kept dry enough to protect the skin, occasionally a tube device which attaches to the penis will prove helpful. These can be obtained at surgical supply and mail-order stores or from the physician. However, they are often unsatisfactory because the penis is constantly wet and can develop swelling and soreness.

There are also objections to putting tubes called *catheters* into the bladder. They predispose to infection, must be changed from time to time, become stopped up, and in rare instances lead to fatal complications. However, they are the lesser evil and can greatly simplify nursing problems. The patient can be kept dry enough to prevent bedsores.

The physician should decide when and if an indwelling catheter is desirable. Some physicians may prescribe a drug to keep down infection while a catheter is in place.

In rare instances a *cystostomy* may be recommended by a physician. This is an opening through the wall of the abdomen into the bladder, which may be necessary if a person cannot tolerate a catheter through the natural passage or if there is a decided tendency to develop bladder stones.

The catheter patient should drink about two quarts of liquid a day to insure an adequate flow of urine. The urine flowing through a catheter may be extremely cloudy and contain excessive mucus. Cloudiness is not necessarily due to pus; it may be due to natural waste which is abundant in wasting patients. Waste may be deposited on the inner wall of the catheter or on the inside of a glass tube that connects to the catheter. This is of little importance as long as the urine flows freely. Eventually, all catheters will become stopped up and need to be replaced. Fresh catheters should be inserted only under the doctor's direction.

The patient who cannot control his bowels is a special nursing problem. The most frequent problem regarding bowels is fecal impaction, an accumulation of hard, putty-like waste material in the rectum. Sometimes a patient will have a fecal impaction with considerable pain in the rectum and the lower abdomen and still have frequent, loose, scanty, watery stools. This is due to a decided urge to have a bowel movement but the ability only to pass liquid around the accumulation. Impactions can be prevented by using mineral oil, enemas, or suppositories to insure regular bowel movements.

Sometimes a person will have fairly regular, normal bowel movements but have no control over their passing. This situation can be treated by putting the patient on a bedpan and giving him an enema before he soils the bed. Or a laxative suppository may be inserted into the rectum, causing the emptying of the rectum in a few minutes.

If an elderly person has difficulty lying or sitting on a bedpan, several thicknesses of newspaper are convenient for keeping the bed from getting soiled.

Disposable plastic gloves, available at drugstores and surgical-supply houses, are convenient for the nurse in dealing with enemas, suppositories, and impactions. In the home, impactions are diagnosed with certainty only by inserting a glove-covered finger into the rectum and feeling the hard material. This is done by thoroughly greasing the gloved finger with soap, vaseline, or surgical lubricant, all of which can be obtained at a drugstore.

Impactions are easiest to handle by preventive measures such as mineral oil, laxatives, enemas, or suppositories.

A feeble old person may get diarrhea. Faulty digestion or a food intolerance may cause it but most often it is due to a germ. Diarrhea may cause incontinence; if it persists for more than a day or so it may require a doctor's examination and test. Several good preparations for diarrhea have been developed in the last ten or twelve years. The old stand-by drugs, such as paregoric, are usually effective.

# ❧ 43 ❧

# Bed Sores: Care and Prevention

*Bedsores* are ulcerations caused by pressure against the bed; they occur in patients confined to bed for long periods. To the inexperienced person the size and severity of these sores can be alarming. The oozing, foul-smelling opening, or ulcer, may go as deep as bone and muscle and be eight inches or more in diameter.

Of course, most bedsores are not that large or severe. More often, they are one or two inches wide and occur over the lower spine, the sides of the hips, or on the heels. Occasionally, they occur where the shoulder blades press against the bed.

The following factors all play a part in the development of bedsores: (1) lying a long time in one position, with pressure on a particular area; (2) wrinkled bedclothing; (3) lack of cleanliness from such causes as excessive perspiration or soiling; (4) poor food intake that interferes with natural body repair; (5) poor circulation such as occurs in many feeble patients.

The patient should be turned often so as to prevent prolonged pressure on any one part of the body. A draw sheet, already mentioned, will simplify turning. The bed-clothing should be kept unwrinkled. The parts where bed-sores are most apt to occur should be inspected, bathed, and powdered twice a day. An incontinent patient should be inspected after each soiling. The patient should have a well-balanced diet. Where possible, the patient should be exercised by bending limbs in rhythm to stimulate circulation.

Special care should be given to areas of the lower back, the hips, or the heels that seem to be discolored. The first sign of a bedsore is a pink or reddened surface over a pressure area. If such a discoloration occurs, the patient should lie in a position in which pressure is minimized.

Among the devices used to keep pressure off discolored skin or bedsores is a rubber "doughnut" which can be bought at most drugstores. This is like the toy floats used by children at swimming pools. Smaller ones can be used to keep pressure from the heels.

Lambskins are soft, soothing, and allow for circulation of air next to the skin. There are mats of synthetic fibers which are nearly as good as lambskins and much cheaper. Foam rubber mats beneath the pressure points of back, hips, or heels will help to prevent bedsores.

No one method of preventing pressure is entirely satisfactory in all circumstances. Ask the doctor's advice.

*Treat the areas before sores develop.* However, in spite of all efforts, small ulcers may occur. The sores most often begin with a dark violet discoloration of the skin with subsequent sloughing, leaving an open sore. Do not apply home remedies to sores. Use only soap and warm water until the doctor advises some other remedy. Intensive treatment is required, and healing is slow. The physician should prescribe for bedsores, but cleanliness and freedom from pressure remain the most important factors in their cure.

# ❦ 44 ❧

# Tubes for Feeding, Breathing, and Other Purposes

If you have visited patients in the hospital, you have undoubtedly seen the application of tubes. One patient can have five or six tubes connected to his body. He may have a tube in his nose for oxygen; he may have another tube passed into his gullet for feeding or emptying the stomach. He may be receiving blood or fluid in a vein through a tube. He may have an indwelling catheter in his bladder. Following an operation, he may have a tube draining the kidney, gall bladder, or the digestive system.

In this chapter I shall try to answer questions about various tubing procedures, and so make the doctor's work easier by providing understanding to those caring for the patient.

What about the elderly patient who will not or cannot eat? Can he be fed? Yes, although the wisdom of such a move may be doubtful. He can be fed by passing a tube through the nose or mouth, through the throat, and into the stomach.

What can be accomplished by force feeding? Certainly to prolong a miserable, unconscious, hopeless life is not a humane reason for tube feeding.

What of the feelings of those who cannot stand the heartrending idea of allowing a loved one to die of starvation?

Is there a chance that the patient will improve so as to be able to take nourishment in the usual way? Does he get any joy whatsoever out of life?

In my own view, tube feeding is justified only in temporary situations, such as recovery from an acute illness or operation where such feeding is essential to recovery. Tube feeding may be used during the acute phase of a stroke.

Stomach tubes should be inserted by a doctor or nurse. These can be clamped when the patient is not being fed. By attaching a small funnel, any amount of food substance can be introduced. There are a number of complete foods available for tube feeding such as are fed to infants from a nipple bottle.

Proper body repair and maintenance of weight are the ideals which should guide tube feeding. For a person of average size this would require about 2,500 calories a day. To maintain a good output of urine to dispose of body wastes, a person would need two to three quarts of liquid, part of which is used to dissolve the food.

Some patients with stomach tubes tend to spit up their food, to become nauseated, or to develop irritation of the nose or throat. By giving small amounts of food five or six times a day instead of larger amounts less often, stomach upset can usually be avoided. Irritation caused by the tube is seldom a serious problem, yet temporary removal of the tube may be necessary.

In many cases, families of patients ask about giving food by vein, and indeed this is done during acute illness.

However, in the very old, who may have weak hearts, continued infusions of food and water by vein can precipitate acute congestive heart failure. Relatives at times insist that a physician give fluids in the vein at home, which could be dangerous.

Another way of introducing food substance and fluid into the body is by *hypodermoclysis*. By this method, needles are introduced beneath the skin, of the thighs usually, and fluid allowed to flow in slowly. It can be a tedious and painful procedure.

Generally, the only way to maintain adequate fluid and food intake in the unconscious or very feeble patient is by stomach tube. It is the safest, most economical way, and does not require special skill after the tube is in place.

Tube drainage of the bladder has already been discussed.

If an old person has gall-bladder trouble it may be necessary to drain bile from the right side of his abdomen after surgery. These tubes are put in one of the bile tubes leading from the liver to the upper intestine to allow bile to flow while the damaged bile tube heals. Drainage of bile helps relieve *jaundice* if that is present. Jaundice is a yellow discoloration of the skin caused by excessive bile in the system due to a stone or other obstruction in the bile tube. Usually bile drainage requires no special care at home, but the physician should be notified if the color or consistency of the bile changes, if the patient develops fever, or if pain occurs in the abdomen near the tube.

Most adults nowadays know about devices whereby oxygen can be given in an emergency. This is done by masks, oxygen tents, and various kinds of tubes. If a person is very sick, with a bluish color of the lips and skin, he may need oxygen. More often, getting oxygen equipment for a hopelessly ill and feeble old person is wasted effort.

The desire to "do something" can hasten the passing of an old person. Let the physician decide whether fluids, oxygen, and various tubes are desirable. A physician's ability is not to be judged by the amount of commotion he causes. Often the wiser course is to do relatively little.

# ❧ 45 ❧

# Dying

The time comes eventually, when none of the suggestions in the previous chapters can provide any real help. Death approaches in spite of all efforts, expense, and patience. To accept death as inevitable and to make it as easy as possible for the departing patient is the reasonable and humane approach.

The aims of medicine are to relieve suffering and to prolong life. Which of these aims should come first in an individual case is often difficult to determine. I believe life should be prolonged, when possible, if a patient can get any satisfaction from living. The satisfaction may be in hearing music, enjoying a child's laughter or a bird's song. It may be in tasting food or simply gazing at a sunset. The difficulty arises when the physician cannot foretell the outcome. If the family allows him to do so, the physician will avoid heroic measures to keep the spark of life aglow in a tired old body. If the physician, who has been present at the bedside of many dying patients, chooses not to inject tube and needle, his decision should cause relief, not panic. Death is, after all, inevitable and frequently a blessing.

If an elderly person has been bedridden a long time, what are the signs that his condition has worsened? They may be any combination of the following:

He becomes quieter and less active. He loses consciousness. He becomes pale and breaks into a cold sweat. Deep, noisy breathing manifests itself. Moisture accumulates in the throat and there may be a gurgling sound in breathing; this is called the "death rattle." The patient develops periodic respiration, in which a lapse of breathing occurs for as long as a minute, followed by increasingly fast and deep breathing for a minute or more before diminishing toward another lapse. This is called *Cheyne-Stokes respiration,* named for two physicians who described the condition in 1818. Such periodic breathing may be temporary during serious illness and may last for weeks but is always a danger sign.

The patient shows evidence of worsening condition when he fails to respond naturally to pain, such as a pinch or a pin prick. If his foot or hand is lifted it may fall back heavily.

This state in a feeble old body does not constitute a medical emergency. If the patient is found weak and pale, the physician should be called, but unless the patient is obviously in severe pain and requires immediate attention, it is not necessary for the doctor to come at once. When he comes, he may decide to put a dying patient in the hospital. It is astonishing at times how tenaciously some old people cling to life. Putting the patient in a hospital may make the end easier for all. But there is no reason to rush a person to the hospital if he has only an hour or so to live. The less commotion surrounding death, the better. Let the doctor decide.

A person with a wasting disease may linger weeks or months, requiring medicine for any rest he may get. As death approaches, someone near and dear to the patient should be trained to give him a hypodermic to relieve suffering or restlessness. A doctor or nurse can instruct anyone who is willing to administer a hypodermic.

With the death rattle, mucus and saliva may be sucked from the throat with an Asepto Syringe to which a four- or five-inch rubber tube is attached extending into the throat.

If a very old person is dying, is not suffering, and the doctor has done all he can, the physician need not be in constant attendance. Years ago, when doctors were not so much in demand as today, they often spent many hours with the family. Nowadays, with the telephone at hand, and more people to take care of, time can be better spent elsewhere than at the bedside of a gradually sinking patient. When a person has been under his care for months or years, and where death is expected, the physician's presence at the time of death or immediately afterward is not required, but he should be notified by telephone.

How is death recognized? The eyes become fixed, with opened pupils which do not respond to light. The heartbeat and breathing cease. The mouth may be open and motionless. The skin turns pale and cold. The skin in contact with the bed may become bluish or purple—*livor mortis*. After thirty to sixty minutes the limp extremities may become stiff—*rigor mortis*.

Death is not an emergency. If you are not sure, wait a few minutes. Remain calm. If there is no change, call the physician.

A note should be made of the approximate time of death. This is needed for the formal papers that the physician must fill out for the state, and insurance companies also require this information.

The physician may request a *postmortem* examination, especially if the patient dies in a hospital. Such examinations are made by an extensive operative procedure; they do not deface the body so far as funeral arrangements are concerned.

A postmortem examination is often helpful to the doctor in guiding his diagnosis and treatment in similar cases. It can be reassuring to the family who may be concerned about contagion or other undiagnosed condition.

Such examinations are usually performed without charge as a service of the hospital by *pathologists* whose specialty this is.

It is wise to agree to a postmortem, unless there are very strong feelings against it. The physician, when he realizes that death is near, may ask permission for a postmortem, not because he is unfeeling, but on the contrary because he doesn't want to cause a disturbance later, when the family is upset by the death.

The death of a person not under the care of a physician must be reported to the official medical examiner or coroner. If a physician is called for the first time to see a dying person, he is bound by law to call the coroner. It is far better to have regular medical attendance than to make a coroner's investigation necessary.

Funeral arrangements are discussed in the following chapter.

# ❦ 46 ❧

# Death and Funeral Arrangements

Sooner or later death comes to all, including those who have received the best of care. It is sad when a loving child cannot accept death even after months or years of time for preparation.

Remember that most old people are not dominated by fear of death; they are tired of age and infirmity if not actual pain. Physicians often talk about death with old people who would welcome it gladly. On a number of occasions I have been called upon to tell an elderly person about the death of an old friend, only to learn that for most of the very old, death causes no real dread.

I think that death can be discussed openly. On the other hand, to dwell on death, dying, and funerals is depressing to anyone. Death dispels much pain, tiredness, and trouble, and when we discuss it, we ought not consider it a curse in all cases.

In civilized countries death should be surrounded with dignity; too often it is not. Weary, nervous, distraught people sometimes make a travesty of death by their exhibition of hysteria, greed, and bitterness. Like creatures of prey, some people stalk the deathbed scene, jealously concerned with their inheritance or with the fear that others might deprive them of it. Many people resent those who may be called upon to supply a burial plot or to decide on a funeral director.

It is sad to see close relatives at the deathbed who will not be civil to each other. These ugly scenes occur too often and should be avoided. I have seen people hanging upon the doctor's words, pleading, "Is there anything we can do, Doctor?" I'd like to reply that I wish those who ask had treated the elderly person with more tenderness, or had got along better, or been less demanding.

Let's say unpleasant scenes are prevented; what next?

At the time legal matters are settled, elderly relatives have definite ideas regarding funeral arrangements and they may be explicit in what they want done, even as to choice of funeral director. Sad as this is, it saves difficult decisions by others.

It is reasonable, however, for a relative who has power of attorney to make funeral arrangements before death occurs. Where several relatives are involved, the nearest kin or the one who had managed the decedent's affairs takes the lead in deciding upon a funeral director.

A capable funeral director will consult the family as to how elaborate and expensive a funeral should be, and how much is to be contributed by each relative when the responsibility is being shared.

I would like to make a plea for simplicity. Expensive caskets and copper vaults buried in the ground accomplish little except to give one a feeling of doing what is "best" for the deceased.

In recent years, more and more individuals have been offered the choice of cremation. The procedure is simple and less expensive. Think about this, and consult the family and the funeral director.

Purchase of a casket is usually made after death. In selecting a casket one should realize that funeral directors are businessmen whose profit is larger on more expensive articles. Costly shrouds, caskets, vaults, and special services are usually not necessary. As in any store, the buyer can without embarrassment ask for a less expensive item.

To make funeral arrangements calmly before death is better than making them anxiously afterward. Funeral directors are also excellent practical psychologists, and being upset can cost you as much as $1,000 extra. Have someone do a little shopping "in advance of need," as the undertakers advise.

The deceased may leave a small estate which relatives feel honor bound to spend entirely on the funeral. Perhaps this is better than a dispute over its division.

Funerals should be an occasion for families joining together in affection; they should not engender bitterness.

After the funeral, the matter of the will arises. Procedures for carrying out the terms of a will vary from state to state and require legal guidance. It is perfectly proper to ask a lawyer in advance about his fee for advice and legal procedure. If it seems unreasonable, other advice can be sought.

# Conclusion

In the foregoing chapters I have tried to introduce you to the elderly as I know them. In a work of this kind, it is necessary to devote more attention to what is wrong than what is right, and perhaps to give the impression that old age itself is a sickness.

Such an attitude would belittle the accomplishments of many able old people whose professional, artistic, and commercial accomplishments are legion; whose kindness, serenity, and sweetness make old age easy to bear for themselves and those around them.

I shall be happy if I have contributed to the comfort of any of my old friends and those who care for them or to that of any other old people and their families. Some of my views are more concerned with feelings than with facts, and another equally conscientious doctor might disagree with me on details of treatment.

I hope, however, that this book will make for better understanding among old people, their relatives, and their doctors, and provide a measure of comfort in time of need.

# APPENDIX

# INDEX

# Appendix: Sources of Help

Chapter 14, "Resources Outside the Family," gives information on seeking help from public and voluntary health and welfare agencies. Reread the "Do's" and "Don'ts" listed there whenever you seek assistance.

The name and address of the national headquarters of each agency are listed as of 1969. Where possible, the number of state and local offices is given. (The number is constantly increasing.) Look in your telephone directory for the address and telephone number of the office nearest you. If it is not listed under the name of the organization, look at the listings for your city, county, or state (your city Office for the Aging; your county Public Health Department; your state Heart Association).

Try to locate in advance a service that you are likely to need; do not wait until an emergency develops. If you cannot find the local agency, write to the national headquarters for information; it should answer within about a month.

Only services of practical use are listed. Services may vary in different localities according to the resources available. I have listed most of the major national sources of help. But there are also many fine small organizations to assist you. Find out if your church, union, or club offers any useful service. Your city's recreation department, public library, and school system may provide information and services. Consider every possibility, and keep yourself informed.

### VOLUNTARY HEALTH AND MEDICAL ASSOCIATIONS

(Organizations for specific diseases or conditions are listed alphabetically by the name of the disease or condition.)

American Medical Association
535 North Dearborn Street
Chicago, Illinois 60610

Has a National Committee for the Aging, with the purpose of stimulating interest and action by the medical profession, and encourages the development of similar committees by state and county societies. Nearly every county in the United States has a local medical society; the one in your county may have an active Committee for the Aging. Ask your doctor about it or contact the Society directly.

Several AMA publications are helpful: *More Life for Your Years*, a fact sheet for older persons, published each month, contains interesting and useful material on all aspects of aging. It can be obtained from the national headquarters.

American National Red Cross
17th and D Streets N.W.
Washington, D.C. 20006

3,400 chapters; represented in every county in the United States, Your local chapter may offer courses on home care for the aged and safety in the home.

Arthritis Foundation
1212 Avenue of the Americas
New York, New York 10036
79 local groups

Service includes a handbook in Spanish and English on arthritis: information and advice on resources for diagnosis, treatment, and rehabilitation; counseling to help meet individual needs.

American Foundation for the Blind
15 West 16th Street
New York, New York 10010

Acts as a clearing house for local and regional agencies serving the blind and deaf-blind. One of its programs is producing talking books. Your public library may furnish information on materials available, such as talking books, Braille, tapes, large-type publications.

American Cancer Society
219 East 42nd Street
New York, New York 10017
58 divisions    3,081 local units

Provides services to cancer patients, including information about the disease, medical supplies, and transportation to clinics.

American Diabetes Association, Inc.
18 East 48th Street
New York, New York 10017
22 state groups    25 local groups

Service includes education in early recognition of diabetes, importance of medical supervision, and in giving the patient a better understanding of his disease.

American Heart Association
44 East 23rd Street
New York, New York 10010
55 affiliates      300 local chapters

Maintains an information service, including facts about heart disease for patients. In 1968 it provided booklets for doctors to give their patients, including: *After the Coronary; Aphasia and the Family; Do It Yourself Again: Self-Help Devices for the Stroke Patient; Facts About Congestive Heart Failure; Heart Disease Caused by Coronary Atherosclerosis; Strokes—A Guide for the Family.* These pamphlets are revised from time to time. Ask your doctor or your local chapter for any you need.

National Association for Mental Health
10 Columbus Circle
New York, New York 10019
49 state divisions      800 local chapters

Serves as a central source for educational materials on mental illness, including pamphlets on *Preparation for Aging,* and *Families of the Mentally Ill.*

National Parkinson Foundation
135 East 44th Street
New York, New York 10017

Information service to Parkinson disease patients and their families.

National Tuberculosis and Respiratory Disease Association
1740 Broadway
New York, New York 10019
56 state groups      1935 local groups

Now concerned with several lung diseases, including bronchitis and emphysema. Has information and referral service.

VOLUNTARY SOCIAL WELFARE ASSOCIATIONS

Council of Jewish Federations and Welfare Funds
729 Seventh Avenue
New York, New York 10019
Over 200 local federations


Family Service Association of America
44 East 23rd Street
New York, New York 10010
About 400 local agencies


National Council of Catholic Charities
1346 Connecticut Avenue N.W.
Washington, D.C. 20036
Many local councils

These three national voluntary social-service agencies provide counseling services and other programs to help meet problems of family living. The local office may refer you to other community resources, depending on your needs.


United Community Funds and Councils of America
345 East 46th Street
New York, New York 10017

2,300 local United Funds, Community Chests, Community Welfare Councils in communities throughout the United States, Canada, Australia, the Philippines, and South Africa. Primarily concerned with fund raising and community planning for the local voluntary health, welfare, and recreation agencies. Each office knows what is available in the community and can refer you to an appropriate agency. Many publish a directory of available services.

SPECIALIZED SERVICES

National Council of Homemaker Service
1790 Broadway
New York, New York 10019

A homemaker service supplies mature, trained, and professionally supervised women to help families in times of illness and stress. Unfortunately, the demand far exceeds the supply.

National Legal Aid and Defender Association
1155 East 60th Street
Chicago, Illinois 60637

Central clearing house for local organizations providing legal aid to persons without means to pay a lawyer. Your local Bar Association may give advice about lawyers in your town.

ASSOCIATIONS FOR THE AGING

American Association of Retired Persons
1225 Connecticut Avenue N.W.
Washington, D.C. 20036

More than 1,000,000 members plus many county chapters. Nation's largest nonprofit organization for Americans fifty-five years of age or older. Offers outstanding health-insurance program, special rates on prescription and other drugs, medical supplies, travel. Participates in national affairs and special interests of older persons. Its publications *Modern Maturity* and *AARP News Bulletin* alone are well worth the $2.00 membership dues.

American Nursing Home Association
1101 17th Street N.W.
Washington, D.C. 20036

Central accrediting agency for nursing homes. Provides a directory.

National Association of Homes for the Aging
49 West 45th Street
New York, New York 10036

Maintains a directory of nonprofit homes for the aged; an accrediting agency to protect and advance the interests of their residents.

National Association of Jewish Homes for the Aged
2525 Centerville Road
Dallas, Texas 75228

Provides information regarding nonprofit homes for the aged, nursing homes, geriatric hospitals, and special facilities for Jewish aged.

National Council on the Aging, Inc.
315 Park Avenue South
New York, New York 10010

Provides a national information and consultation center. Works with other organizations to develop interest in problems of older people.

National Council of Senior Citizens
1627 K Street N.W.
Washington, D.C. 20006

Organization of 2000 autonomous senior citizens' clubs and other groups, with a combined membership of more than 2 million individuals. An educational and action group which supports programs to aid older people.

### PUBLIC HEALTH AND WELFARE AGENCIES

United States Department of Health, Education, and Welfare (HEW), Washington, D.C.

REGIONAL OFFICES

Region 1: Connecticut, Maine, Massachusetts, New Hampshire, Rhode Island, Vermont

John F. Kennedy Building, Government Center
Boston, Massachusetts 02203

Region 2: Delaware, New Jersey, New York, Pennsylvania
Room 1005, 26 Federal Plaza
New York, New York 10007

Region 3: District of Columbia, Kentucky, Maryland, Virginia, West Virginia, Puerto Rico, Virgin Islands
220 7th Street N.E.
Charlottesville, Virginia 22901

Region 4: Alabama, Florida, Georgia, Mississippi, North Carolina, South Carolina, Tennessee
50 7th Street N.E.
Atlanta, Georgia 30323

Region 5: Illinois, Indiana, Michigan, Ohio, Wisconsin
433 West Van Buren Street
Chicago, Illinois 60607

Region 6: Iowa, Kansas, Minnesota, Missouri, Nebraska, North Dakota, South Dakota
601 East 12th Street
Kansas City, Missouri 64106

Region 7: Arkansas, Louisiana, New Mexico, Oklahoma, Texas
1114 Commerce Street
Dallas, Texas 75202

Region 8: Colorado, Idaho, Montana, Utah, Wyoming
9017 Federal Office Building
19th and Stout Streets
Denver, Colorado 80202

Region 9: Alaska, Arizona, California, Hawaii, Nevada, Oregon, Washington, Guam, American Samoa
Federal Office Building
50 Fulton Street
San Francisco, California 94102

Two divisions of the Department which are concerned with the needs and problems of the elderly are the Social Security Administration and the recently established Administration on Aging.

### Social Security Administration

There are about 700 district offices in the United States. They provide information and help regarding Medicare, including home health benefits, as well as on all other Social Security benefits. To find your district office, look in the telephone book under: United States Government, Health, Education, and Welfare (Dept. of), Social Security Administration District Office. If there is no district office listed for your community, write the nearest regional office of HEW (see preceding list) and ask for the address of the nearest district office. Call or write the district office for information or an appointment. The district office will supply copies of *Medicare Handbook* (revised annually), which explains in detail how the system works, and will also provide information on what facilities are approved by Medicare, help in filling out forms, and other services.

### Administration on Aging

Originating with the Older American Act of 1965, this division grants money to public and private agencies to meet local needs by coordinating existing programs and planning and developing new ones. By February 1968 grants had been made to 644 organizations, 387 of which offer information, referral, and counseling services. Some of these are state agencies, some city. Look in the telephone book under your city, state, or both for Aging, Office of the. If you do not find one, write the nearest HEW regional office and ask for the location of the nearest counseling and information center operating under the Administration on Aging. This is a growing program; check with your Social Security district office or other agencies listed here to keep informed on developments in your area.

STATE AND COMMUNITY PUBLIC HEALTH SERVICES

Nearly every city and county in the United States has a public health department, listed in the telephone book under the city or state. These provide a variety of services for which your aged relative may be eligible. Some of the home health services provided under Medicare are given by health department staff when prescribed by a physican.

# Index

abdomen
    bloating of, 87
    growths on, 93
    pain in, 86, 87
    *See also* digestive disorders
acceptance, rejection and, 11–13
accidents, prevention of, 100–3
    *See also specific accidents;* living quarters
acute illness in the old, 99–100
    *See also specific illnesses*
Administration on Aging, 47
agitated depression, definition of, 71–72
alcoholism, 109
American Cancer Society, 47, 167
American Heart Association, 47, 168
anemia, 41, 64, 95, 97–98
angina pectoris, causes of, 84, 96
apartments for the aged, 119
aphasia, definition of, 104
apoplexy, 69
appendicitis, 87, 99
appointments with doctors, 64–67
    *See also* house calls
arteries, hardening of, 95, 96
arteriograms, definition of, 125
arteriosclerosis, definition of, 96

arthritis
    hypertrophia, 91
    rheumatoid, 91
    symptoms of, 69
    treatments for, 55, 67
Arthritis Foundation, 47, 167
asthma, 85
atherosclerosis, definition of, 96
auditory nerves, deterioration of, 82
    *See also* hearing disorders
authority
    of household, 26–29, 50–53
    of old people, 68, 78–79
automobile driving, 51
availability of doctors, 56–57, 64

$B_{12}$, use of, 67
backs
    pains in, 89–91
    rounded, 96
balance, sense of, 82
bathroom, arrangements of, 36
    locks in, 101
bed for patient, 35–36, 139–40
    making of, 140
bed sores, 142, 146, 149–50
bedpan, use of, 36, 141
behavior, understanding of, 7–9
    *See also specific behavioral problems*

175

# About the Author

William D. Poe is Associate Clinical Professor of Medicine, the University of North Carolina School of Medicine, and Physician, Student Health Service, U.N.C. He is also Attending Physician at the Methodist Retirement Home, Durham, North Carolina. For eighteen years, he was in private medical practice and made thousands of house calls. He is an Associate of the American College of Physicians and a former Chief of Staff and Chief of Medical Service of Jefferson Hospital, Roanoke, Virginia.